DYMAXION AIROCEAN WORLD

R. BUCKMINSTER FULLER & SHOJI SADAO, CARTOGRAPHERS

EDGES OF ICOSA TRIANGLES EQUAL TO:
63° 26'
3,806 NAUTICAL MILES
8½ JET AIRCRAFT HOURS
14 CONVENTIONAL AIRCRAFT HOURS
7 SHIP DAYS

Books by Sidney Rosen

GALILEO AND THE MAGIC NUMBERS

DOCTOR PARACELSUS

THE HARMONIOUS WORLD OF JOHANN KEPLER

WIZARD OF THE DOME

R. Buckminster Fuller, Designer for the Future

WIZARD
OF THE
DOME

Buckminster Fuller with a model of a Tensegrity Mast

WIZARD

OF THE

DOME.

R. Buckminster Fuller,

Designer for the Future

BY SIDNEY ROSEN

LITTLE, BROWN AND COMPANY

BOSTON   TORONTO

The author wishes to thank the editors of the Southern Illinois University
Press for permission to use quotations from the following publications: *No
More Secondhand God* by R. Buckminster Fuller, Copyright © 1963 by
Southern Illinois University Press; and *Education Automation* by R. Buck-
minster Fuller, Copyright © 1962 by Southern Illinois University Press.

Photos Courtesy R. Buckminster Fuller

Contents

	A Beginning	ix
1	Growing Up in New England	3
2	First Failures, First Successes	13
3	A Year of Decision	36
4	The Birth of DYMAXION	50
5	Great Ideas, but Bad Luck	67
6	The Corncrib That Became a House	82
7	The House That Failed	101
8	Nature's Own Geometry	106
9	Geodesic Domes for the World	120
10	Success at Sixty	137
11	Bucky Fuller, Poet and Prophet	151
12	Living Space for *World Man*	162
	The End — but Not the End	182
	Bibliography	185
	Index	187

A Beginning

IN THE CITY of Kabul, capital of the country of Afghanistan, a miracle was taking place.

There, on the grounds of the 1956 International Trade Fair, a great domed structure was rising. The men who were rapidly bolting together its aluminum ribs were illiterate Afghans. They knew nothing about the techniques of building construction and spoke only their native language. The single engineer who directed them had issued simple instructions: "Bolt blue ends to blue ends and red ends to red ends."

That was all.

Two days later, the workmen found to their amazement that they had built a great dome fashioned of aluminum triangles and covered with a skin of nylon cloth. This palatial hemisphere had risen faster than the fabled pleasure domes of Kubla Khan. Completed, it was to be the American Pavilion at the Fair, a structure a thousand times more dramatic than the machinery for show it was to house. Inside and outside the dome men of many nations stood and gazed and wondered.

"What is that strange house?"

"The Americans call it a *geodesic* dome. They say all the parts were flown to Kabul in a single airplane!"

"Can it be true that it was designed and manufactured in less than a month's time?"

"They say that the triangle pattern of the dome makes it stronger than larger and heavier square steel buildings. But all those aluminum pieces weigh only ninety-two hundred pounds! Isn't that much too light for a house that size?"

"Look how much time we had to spend getting the parts from Moscow and putting our Pavilion together — months!"

"Who is the architect? What American created this fantastic design?"

The same questions were asked in other great cities of the world, when other huge geodesic domes were flown in and assembled for Trade Fairs. At each Fair, the spherical network of triangles assembled by native workers on the spot in an amazingly brief time drew visitors as apple blossoms draw bees.

Who was the architect of the dome? Who had created the design?

He was a man who had never graduated from a school of architecture. Nor had he ever been certified as a professional architect. He was an American who had spent most of his life thinking about the ways in which man's ability to master nature could best be used to solve all the problems of mankind on earth. He had even invented a name for this kind of thinking. He called it *World Design Science.*

His name was R. Buckminster Fuller.

WIZARD

OF THE

DOME

1

Growing Up in New England

RICHARD BUCKMINSTER FULLER, JR., was born in Milton, Massachusetts, in 1895.

It was a time when the countries of the modern world had begun to separate into two groups, the rulers and the ruled. The larger, richer nations had built great navies, and had used their fighting ships to acquire land that was thousands of miles away. Even the United States, the "land of the free," was now taking over foreign territory that was being colored "American Possession" in the geography books. It was the finest hour of great empires.

It was also the year when a German scientist named Wilhelm Roentgen, while experimenting with the discharge of an electrical spark through an evacuated glass tube, accidentally stumbled upon the source of x-rays. And in 1896, the next year, when Bucky Fuller had reached the ripe old age of one, a French physicist named Henri Becquerel set the scientific world on fire by discovering that an ore of the chemical element uranium gave off a strange, powerful radiation, a phenomenon he called radioactivity. Buckminster Fuller was born when the century was about to change, and when

man's understanding of his universe was about to change,
too.

The Fuller name was well-known in Massachusetts history. Bucky's great, great, great, great grandfather,
Thomas Fuller, had been a lieutenant in the British Navy
who had sailed for the New World with the Puritans in
1630. All the Fullers, from Thomas down, had been
strong-willed and resolute. Timothy Fuller, the grandson
of Thomas, had become an ordained minister in Boston.
When the colonies were in the process of putting together
the document that was to become the Constitution of the
United States, Timothy was the Massachusetts delegate to
the Federal Constitutional Assembly. He had read the finished document and then had made an impassioned
speech against accepting the Constitution without a provision for the prohibition of human slavery. When the
provision was voted down, Timothy had refused to sign
the Constitution.

Bucky's grandfather, Arthur Buckminster Fuller, was
also a minister. Like Timothy, he dared to stand against
popular opinion. Arthur preached for the abolition of
slavery before the Civil War. When the terrible conflict
between the States began, he joined the Union Army
as a chaplain. But was that enough for a Fuller? Not
content to be just a man who listened to the problems
of soldiers, Grandfather Arthur led a charge across the
river at bloody Fredericksburg and, in victory, was shot
dead.

And then there was Bucky's great-aunt, Margaret
Fuller. In 1840, a time when it was considered dangerous for a woman to think about anything other than keep-

ing house and taking care of babies, she became the editor of a famous literary magazine, *The Dial*. Her friends were people like Henry Thoreau and Ralph Waldo Emerson, all famous, all independent thinkers. She was a strong, intelligent woman, self-reliant and tough, and always ready to help genius to flourish. She sailed to Italy and married an Italian marquis there. Even in Europe, her strong spirit showed itself. In 1848, when the city of Rome was being besieged by the French army, she took charge of one of the hospitals. Margaret's death was a sad one. On June 16, 1850, the ship in which she, her husband, and her child were returning to New York foundered in a storm, almost within sight of the harbor toward which they had been sailing. Almost all the hands and passengers perished.

With such a heritage, it was no wonder that Bucky Fuller was a strong-willed child who did not give up easily in the face of difficulties. And he began to encounter problems almost from the first.

Most serious was the problem of his vision. Bucky had been born with abnormally farsighted vision, which made him look cross-eyed. But this defect had not been discovered until he reached the age of four. Up to that year, when he was first fitted with corrective glasses, the world had been a kind of large colored blur for Bucky. He could only make out very large patterns — trees, houses, and outlines of people. The details were lost. He recalled later in life, "I did not see a human eye or a teardrop or a human hair until I was four years old!"

Once he was fitted with the thick, owlish lenses he was to wear the rest of his life, Bucky began to be aware of

details. Nevertheless, he never lost his dependence upon
the large-pattern clues to the world about him. This happened even in school.

At Milton Academy, where Bucky was sent to school,
boys were prepared to enter Harvard University — and
no bones about it! Apart from the many hours of class-
work and study, Milton Academy boys were expected to
participate in athletics. Bucky was short and stocky,
and he chose football. It was not easy for an opposing
lineman to knock him over in a game. And Bucky could
run surprisingly fast for a short boy. Having to play
without his glasses was the worst ordeal; the outside
world swam before him in a kind of mist. But again, the
ability to recognize large patterns came to his rescue. He
recognized his teammates by their general outlines and
behavior; all others were the opposing team. However, if
the other side wore jerseys of about the same color,
Bucky had trouble distinguishing friend from foe.

Bucky enjoyed school, and he loved mathematics best.
He could not understand why some of his teachers resented the questions he asked in class. He always seemed
to rub his teachers the wrong way.

When his math teacher introduced the class to geometry, she placed a chalk point on the blackboard and explained that even though this kind of mark might be
called a point, there was really no such thing as a point
— it was just an imaginary idea. Then she drew a line
and said that the line was made up of a large number of
these imaginary points placed side by side.

Bucky found it difficult to understand why the teacher
would draw a real line on the board and then say it was

made up of things that weren't there. Then, she made things worse by drawing two sets of parallel lines that crossed each other. These lines made up a *plane*, or a surface that had length and width, but no depth. Planes, too, were imaginary. Finally, she showed how planes could be stacked up, one atop the other, to give a solid figure with length, width, and depth. The solid figure she drew on the blackboard had all equal sides, and she called it a *cube*.

This was too much for Bucky. He raised his hand and informed the teacher that if the cube was made up of points that were imaginary that made up a set of lines that were imaginary that made up planes that were imaginary, then the cube wasn't there at all, and how could she draw it? Futhermore, he wanted to know how much the cube weighed and if it was hot or cold.

The result of that little incident was that Bucky had to force himself to stop asking questions in his mathematics class. Though he got into occasional trouble by saying things in class that seemed outrageous, he passed all his courses, especially science, with flying colors. The only course in which he didn't get an A was Latin, a language he could never get himself to like. By his junior year, he had managed to make quarterback on the football team. This position gave him a certain amount of prestige. It was no longer necessary to defend himself against those cruel classmates who used to call him "four-eyes." Like the other students, he began to appreciate the inner strength that a school like Milton Academy gave through its long-established traditions and attitudes. With the other boys, he felt a deep affection for the Academy. But, as much as he liked school, he loved the summers more. For summer meant vacation. And vacation meant Bear Island in Maine!

Bear Island! It was a genuine paradise. Bucky's grandmother had purchased it — a real island in Penobscot Bay — in 1904, along with two other islands. On Bear Island, there were beautiful pebble beaches that sloped upward through spruce groves to a large central hill. You had to wear sneakers when you went bathing, because the spines of the sea urchins on the sea bottom were long and sharp. And the waters of Penobscot Bay were icy cold, even on the hottest summer day.

Often, as he looked out to sea, Bucky had seen a comic, moustached face lift dripping out of the water — a real live seal! Usually, there was a staring contest, boy and seal regarding each other intently for what seemed like hours, but was probably only seconds. Then, with a faint plop, the whiskered head would disappear. Bucky was in love with Bear Island and with the sea.

On the central hill of the island the frame of a house began to take shape. The house had been designed by a well-known Boston architect, the son of the great poet, Henry Wadsworth Longfellow. It stood high on the hill, with the sea visible from three sides. To the family, it became "The Big House." All the materials for the house, wood, glass, and nails, had been ferried over from the mainland eleven miles away in the old schooner *Polly*, out of Boston. There was a romantic ship! She had been a privateer during the war of 1812, and now, almost a century later, was still in service.

The Penobscot Bay islands had been settled during the

early years of colonial America. The Fullers found many gravestones on Bear Island, some almost a hundred and fifty years old. One of the interesting things that had happened on the island about three years before Bucky's grandmother bought it was the coming of the members of a religious group called the Seventh-Day Adventists. All the members of this sect in the city of Bangor had rowed out to Bear Island one day, and had climbed up into the trees to await the end of the world. After the time of the predicted disaster had safely passed, the Adventists had climbed down from the trees and had rowed back to the mainland. Why had they chosen Bear Island? No one knew.

On the island, traditions of living were established that were to remain a long time. Every visitor, whether family, friend, or stranger, had to write his name in the guest book. Every summer, Bucky would write his name a different way. He tried: Richard Buckminster Fuller, Richard B. Fuller, Richard (Bucky) Fuller, and R. Buckminster Fuller. He finally decided that this last combination was the most striking, and from then on always signed his name as R. Buckminster Fuller.

At night, the family would gather in the living room of The Big House by the great stone fireplace. The kerosene lamp would be lighted and a fire started. Even in the summer Penobscot Bay nights were sure to be cold. Plans would be made for the following day's activities: which lobster pots would be put out, or which neighboring island would be visited.

One of the luxuries in The Big House was a phonograph, wound by hand, that played thick wax records.

How to store the flat discs was a constant problem. If they were simply stacked, it was difficult to locate a particular one. Also, stacking could cause the lower discs to be warped by the pressure of those on top. Bucky thought about this problem for a while; then he designed and built a record holder out of wire strips. These strips were arranged to make pockets in which the individual records could stand on edge and be popped in and out with ease.

But most important to Bucky during the days spent on Bear Island was the sea. Sailing came to him as naturally as breathing. He spent most of his leisure time on the waters around the island. Each morning his important job was to row about two miles over to Eagle Island for the mail — a round trip of four miles. Bucky enjoyed rowing, but he began to be irritated by the number of times he had to turn his head around in order to see if he was on course. Anyone who has ever rowed a boat knows that the rower's back is always turned toward the direction in which the boat is heading. If the weather was foggy, or if the waters were choppy, Bucky had to turn his head at ten-second intervals in order to make sure of his heading.

How could he propel a boat forward without an engine and yet be able to face forward? Bucky sat up nights thinking. He drew neat little plans on paper and threw them away. One night, he began to think about the little jellyfish that were so common in the Bay waters. How did one of those jellyfish move? It opened and closed itself, like a little umbrella, pushing the water one way and moving in the opposite direction. Could he fashion some kind of instrument that would imitate the jellyfish?

Bucky began to sketch out his thoughts. He fashioned a kind of umbrella on a pole; but it was an inverted umbrella, shaped like a cone. Pushing the pole forward would make the umbrella open and push on the water. If he did this in the stern of the boat, the boat would move forward in the direction opposite to the push. Pulling on the pole would simply collapse the umbrella, which would then slide easily back through the water and be ready for the next push.

The next day, Bucky assembled tools and materials. From the sawing and hammering, there emerged a web-like contraption at the end of a long pole. He screwed a large iron ring into the stern of the rowboat and pulled the pole through it, so that the umbrella would be in the water. Anxiously, he pushed the boat away from the pier and lifted the end of the pole. Here was the test.

Push — the umbrella opened. Pull — it closed. With ease, the rowboat slid out of the harbor into deep water. Bucky found that steering was a simple matter; all you had to do was push the pole a bit to one side or the other. Across the channel to Eagle Island, he push-pulled his umbrella with ease, never once having to turn his head. He made the usual trip for the mail and back in about half the time it had taken him to row.

Inventing became one of Bucky's passions. First he would carefully design on paper whatever he was going to make, and then, with a pocket knife, or other tools, he would go to work. Sometimes it would be a little model sailboat for his little sister Rosy; at other times it might be a glider that would soar on the wind, or a model house with unusual, original features, as walls that opened outward on hinges. In December of 1903, when Bucky was eight, the Wright brothers had accomplished the unthinkable; they had flown the first gasoline-powered airplane over the sand dunes of Kitty Hawk. Now, airplanes were always in Bucky's thoughts. His clever fingers were always whittling and patching bits of wood into model planes. It seemed to him that before long, flying would make all other ways of travel seem ancient.

So it was on Bear Island, that tiny speck of land in Penobscot Bay where the tide rose and fell fifteen feet each day, that the boy named Bucky Fuller began to be conscious of the ways in which man used his technical knowledge to overcome the challenges posed by nature. All the activities that were going on about him — boat building, boat repairing, fishing with lobster pots, drags, nets, and traps — he saw as things that men did in order to survive in the particular place they lived. With a flash of early understanding, he realized that men were able to survive most successfully not merely by using the tools and experience they already had, but by designing new tools and new ways of using them.

Bucky had already begun to think in those patterns of original design that were to shape the events of his later life.

2

First Failures, First Successes

WHEN BUCKY WAS THIRTEEN years old, his father, Richard Fuller, died.

Richard had been the first Fuller to choose a business career, instead of the ministry or law. In those days Boston was a teeming seaport, where tall-masted schooners sailed in from all over the world with cargoes of exotic goods. Fishing boats in great numbers, gliding in beside the quays to deposit catches of haddock, mackerel, and cod, filled the harbor, while the sea gulls coasted overhead, screaming and fighting for tidbits.

Bucky's father had an importing company whose offices were near India Wharf on the Boston waterfront. Bucky loved to visit the warehouse, where there were great teak chests lined with lead and filled with many different kinds of rich-smelling teas from Ceylon, India and China.

Suddenly Bucky found himself the man of the house. There were new chores that became his responsibility. After all her husband's business affairs were settled, Bucky's mother discovered that she would have to get along on far less money than before. She was a resource-

ful and energetic woman, and she worried about Bucky
very much. He was always in some kind of trouble in
school and he never seemed to be able to keep from
spending money foolishly. Nights she would read him
long lectures on changing his ways; and she often asked
the men of the Fuller clan, Bucky's "uncles," to lecture
him also. Her greatest worry was that Bucky would be a
failure in life.

In the month of June, 1913, Bucky graduated from
Milton Academy. All the Fuller men had attended Harvard University and Bucky was to be no exception. His
marks at Milton had been mostly A's, good enough for
him to be accepted at Harvard. A family conference was
held, and it was decided that enough money could be
pooled to pay for Bucky's tuition and living expenses at
college.

That September, Bucky entered his Cambridge dormitory for the first time. When he walked over to Harvard Yard, the brick wall that enclosed this central part
of the university seemed to isolate him from the rest of
the town of Cambridge. The Yard was like an island in
the waters of Penobscot Bay. Squirrels unafraid of man
ran down the trunks of tall elm trees and scampered
across the grass. Other freshmen, like Bucky, were arriv-
ing, bags in hand, to live in that new world. Were they
frightened, he wondered. How different would college be
from Milton Academy? Suddenly his family seemed too
far away for comfort.

Then he shook his head angrily. What kind of nonsense was this for a man! Here at Harvard was the challenge, and he, Bucky Fuller, was not afraid. Back in his

room, he opened his suitcase with steady hands and began to lay out his possessions.

But from the beginning, things went badly for Bucky at Harvard. First, he did not go on in mathematics, the area where he had excelled at Milton Academy, simply because that subject seemed to be a game almost too easy to bother with. Later, he realized that the courses he had chosen did not interest him as much as mathematics.

What was most crushing for Bucky at Harvard was to discover that his classmates separated themselves into different levels of friendship — and that these levels seemed to be determined mainly by how rich one's parents were. Compared to the boys from Milton Academy who had entered Harvard at the same time, Bucky was really a poor boy. The ones who had been so friendly before now deserted him. Even the boy who had been his best friend at Milton chose to room with someone else.

Bucky could cope with difficulties in the classroom; but he did not know what to do about the snobs who would not share their lives with him in the Harvard Yard. There were a few social clubs which, like fraternities, invited freshmen of the "correct" families to join. These clubs became the only basis for friendships among the students who joined them.

"Sorry, Bucky, old boy," said one of his friends of the Milton Academy days, "but it looks as though you're not going to make any of the clubs here."

And so Bucky found himself out of the social swim at Harvard. Though he lived in one of the Yard dormitories, his snobbish dormitory mates treated him like a despised commuter, a student who lived at home, rode the streetcars to and from Harvard Square daily, and who ate his lunch out of a paper bag while sitting in some corner of one of the college buildings.

It did not take very long for college to become a harrowing nightmare for Bucky. One day he decided he had had enough. Without thinking of the consequences, he ran to the bank and withdrew all the money that had been deposited by the family for his semester expenses. Back in his room, he threw some clothes into a suitcase and called a taxi. An hour later, he was on a train, moving out of the Back Bay Station of Boston, bound south for New York City. As he watched the houses flying past his window, Bucky meditated on the folly of his flight; it was the week of midyear examinations. Then he shrugged and pushed all thoughts of Harvard out of his mind.

Bucky checked into one of the better hotels in midtown Manhattan and prepared to enjoy his escape to the fullest. In New York City it was easy to indulge in his bad habit of spending money easily. The first evening he went to the theater and saw the famous dancer of the Ziegfeld Follies, Marilyn Miller. Somehow he contrived to meet her and invited her to dinner. With flashy self-confidence, he also invited all of the girls who danced in the chorus line to join them.

It was fun! How Bucky enjoyed being surrounded by those beautiful girls. The waiters bowed and poured champagne. Everyone treated him like a grown-up and not a boy. The bright lights of Broadway held Bucky captive. He entertained show people every night, until he ran out of cash. Then he continued to live his heady night life and simply charged everything to the Fuller family in Boston.

Eventually Bucky realized he would have to return and face the realities of Harvard Square. He managed to borrow enough money for the fare back to Cambridge. In his mailbox at the dormitory he found a note asking him to call at the Dean's office.

There his reception was far from cordial. Harvard students, said the Dean, were not in the habit of deserting their posts during the week of examinations. No, the Dean did not care to hear excuses or explanations. A Harvard student was expected to be mature enough to have self-discipline and responsibility for his actions. Mr. Fuller did not seem to possess either of these two qualities. The Dean suggested that Mr. Fuller might be happier elsewhere.

Again there was a family conference. Something had to be done with Buckminster, something that would teach him a lesson and change his ways. One of Bucky's rich cousins had a solution: he owned a cotton mill in the province of Quebec, Canada. It might be good for Bucky to have a taste of hard labor for a while; then he might appreciate the benefits of going to college. The uncles and aunts nodded in agreement. Yes, that was the very thing. Pack him off to Canada at once.

At the cotton mill, Bucky was assigned to the job of apprentice to a group of machine fitters. He felt horribly guilty about his New York escapade and resolved to make it up to his mother and the family by working as hard as he could. What he did not expect to happen was

the wave of excitement that came over him when he saw
the long banks of great factory machines that clashed
and roared, fashioning cotton threads into rolls of cloth.

Instead of a chore, this work became a fascinating
pleasure. Bucky began to ask questions of the master mechanics, under whose supervision he tended the machines. Slowly, the complex world of moving mechanical
parts began to make sense to him. Little by little, he grew
to understand the ideas upon which these machines were
based and built. It seemed a miracle to him that the complicated arrangement of levers and wheels designed by
human beings could outwork human hands and fingers
with ease. In Canada, Bucky fell in love with technology.

The reports from the cotton mill back to the family
were excellent. The Fuller "uncles" met again and decided that Bucky would be given another chance at Harvard. When the call to return came, Bucky was somewhat
reluctant to leave the machines he had come to love. But
again, suitcase in hand, he passed through the black iron
gates set in the red brick walls of the Harvard Yard.

This time, life at Harvard was even worse. The new
freshmen were all strangers. Bucky found he had no pa-
tience with professors talking on and on in the lecture
halls. College seemed to be made up of memorizing
words and giving them back in examination books. He
had few friends. The divisions based on snobbery still
existed. Soon he fell back into his old careless ways. He
spent money recklessly and let his studies slide.

This time when the summons came from the Dean, the
tone was more ominous. Bucky was told that he had
wrecked his last chance to stay at the University. It was

obvious that Harvard and Buckminster Fuller were not suited to each other. This dismissal would be final.

To his astonishment, Bucky found that he felt more relieved than guilty. He was aware of the intense disappointment of his mother and the "uncles." But when he indicated that he would be glad to return to the factory in Canada, the tension was eased. He worked at his old job for some months, and then decided to find work in the United States. The city he chose was New York.

His first job was a simple and physical one. He became a meat-lugger for Armour and Company, the large meat-packing corporation. Meat-lugging consisted of carrying great sides of beef from one place to another in the factory. Though he was shorter than most of the other meat-luggers, Bucky's stocky frame enabled him to match strength with them. At first he worked on the night shift. During the day he slept, ate and read books. His keen mind and spirit of enterprise was soon spotted by his superiors, and he was promoted to the position of assistant cashier, with an increase in responsibility and pay.

While Bucky Fuller was in the process of changing his life, events on the continent of Europe were causing profound changes in world history. In the Bosnian capital city of Sarajevo (now in the country called Yugoslavia), the visiting Austrian Archduke Francis Ferdinand was shot and killed by a Serbian patriot named Gavrilo Princip. This assassination sparked the explosion that historians were to call the First World War. By 1916 the Allied and German armies were deadlocked on either side of a line of trenches that ran from the English

Channel to Switzerland in western Europe, and from the Baltic Sea near Riga to the eastern edge of what is now Czechoslovakia in the east.

The new technology of the twentieth century began to change the ways of warfare. The automobile and the airplane were introduced as war machines, first as aids to transportation and observation, and then as machines of death in the form of tanks and fighter planes.

The United States tried to remain a neutral country at first. However, the apparently ruthless sinking of American ships by German submarines, plus a natural feeling of alliance with England, Germany's enemy, changed the attitude of most Americans. In April, 1917, the United States entered the war on the side of the Allies.

The young men of America rushed to enlist in the armed forces, and Bucky Fuller was no exception. In New York, he tried to enlist in the Navy, but he was unable to pass the eye examination. When he tried to fake his way through the required eye tests, his clumsy efforts were easily detected by the examining physicians.

One evening at a party Bucky met a beautiful, dark-haired girl who seemed to be willing to listen patiently to all his ideas about the world. She was Anne Hewlett, the oldest of ten children. Her father was a well-known architect and painter, James Monroe Hewlett. Bucky found himself unable to forget Anne; he called and arranged to see her again. After a few such meetings, Bucky decided that this was the girl he was going to marry.

In the matter of getting into the Navy, Bucky was persistent. And he found a way. The Navy had a great need for small boats to patrol and scout the coastal waters of the Atlantic. Bucky asked for and received his mother's permission to offer her boat, the *Wego,* to the Navy as a patrol boat at Bar Harbor in Maine. He and a close friend, Lincoln Pierce, ran the *Wego* up to the Maine Naval Station. To their great delight, the Navy not only accepted the boat, but took them also. Bucky was put in command of the *Wego,* with Lincoln as first mate. Later Bucky's younger brother, Wolcott, was assigned to the *Wego* as a crew member. Though she was the smallest ship in the Bar Harbor fleet, the *Wego,* under Bucky's command, performed valiantly.

That same summer, Bucky and Anne Hewlett were married. A few months later, Bucky was transferred to the Naval Air Station at Hampton Roads, Virginia. There he was put in command of a fleet of crash boats. His own flagship was a trim craft named the *Inca.*

Hampton Roads was a training base for seaplane pilots. One of the most dangerous moments of a flight occurred when landing on water. If the pontoons of a plane struck the water at the wrong angle, the plane would flip forward with a motion called "porpoising" (like the nose-down movement of porpoises rolling in and out of the water). When this happened, it was the job of the boats in Bucky's fleet to dash out and rescue the pilot as soon as possible. Unfortunately, porpoising resulted too often in the plane's landing upside down in the water, with the pilot strapped in the cockpit upside down and underwater. Many pilots were stunned by the crash and were unable to unbelt themselves at once. By the time a crash boat reached the plane and swimmers had dived in to free him, the pilot had drowned.

Helplessly standing by while such a tragedy occurred was a terrible experience for Bucky, and he began to brood about the problem. Out of many sleepless nights, hundreds of doodles on scratch pads, and conversations with pilots came an idea which he converted into precise engineering drawings. Bucky invented an instrument that could be attached easily to a crash boat, and that could lift a flipped seaplane from the water in time to prevent the pilot's death.

The machine was a kind of grappling hook attached to a boom that projected from an auxiliary mast set in the desk of the crash boat. Within seconds after reaching the scene of a crash, the grappling hook could be attached to hoist the plane quickly from the water. Bucky asked for a hearing and explained his invention to his superior officers. They were impressed enough to order a test set of grappling equipment to be built from his plans.

Bucky's lifesaving hook worked perfectly, from the simulated crash test to the first real crash, where the pilot was hauled dripping, but alive, from the cockpit. The officers of Bucky's command were delighted; in spite of his poor eyesight, this Buckminster Fuller was quite a fellow! As a reward, Bucky was commissioned an ensign and ordered to report to the Naval Academy at Annapolis. There he was to take special courses in mathematics and engineering.

Though it meant that they would be separated for a while, Anne was delighted by the news of Bucky's recognition. She knew how disappointed the Fuller family had been by the two failures at Harvard University. Now the Navy was giving Bucky another chance.

Meanwhile, something important was happening inside Bucky's brain. He had begun to think again about geometry, the subject in which he had excelled at Milton Academy. But now his thoughts were forming in a new way. From the aft deck of his moving ship, he could see the wake — a long line of white bubbles, forming at the propeller and foaming to the surface. These bubbles were all spheres, and Bucky remembered that in geometry, in order to make a sphere the number *pi* had to be used. And at Milton, he had learned that *pi* was a number that ran on and on and on to hundreds of places after the decimal — an *irrational* number.

Why, he thought to himself, would nature use a number that had no ending? That meant that every form in nature that was part of a sphere or a circle, or was rounded in some way, depended for its existence on a never-ending number. It didn't make sense. Bucky felt that nature would never use this kind of geometry. He decided then and there that the *pi* geometry might be all right for textbooks, but that nature had no use for numbers like *pi*; she built her forms in a different way, using only whole numbers.

What was that different way? Bucky knew that in chemistry, nature seemed to use whole numbers in building up molecules of matter. Why couldn't there be an entire geometry of nature, much simpler than the geometry worked out by man? Bucky decided that he would like to spend the rest of his life finding out the system of nature's own geometry.

His studies at Annapolis taught him more. He began to see a pattern in the way man was steadily increasing his chances of surviving in the midst of natural forces that opposed this survival. Progress in science and technology was the record of how man had learned to use to his advantage certain principles and laws of behavior he had discovered in nature. Bucky had become familiar with modern machine tools. He realized that the entire history of toolmaking reflected two things: first, all of man's past experiences in making things; secondly, and more important, how man was being stimulated into looking ahead to the needs of the future.

Buckminster Fuller was beginning to see the large-pattern clues to the universe about him.

During the following year, 1918, Bucky was promoted to lieutenant. And, to his great delight, he became a father. He and Anne called their new daughter Alexandra. However, the war was coming to an end, and Bucky was kept busy at many tasks. He had little time to spend with his family. One job, which gave him some experience in writing, was to be editor of the newspaper, *Transport.* This paper was published at sea for the men of the Transport Force of the Atlantic Fleet. Then, right after the Armistice was signed on November 11, Bucky was given a fascinating and historic assignment.

He was ordered to report to the battleship U.S.S. *George Washington,* which was to carry President Woodrow Wilson to France to attend the Paris Peace Conference. This was the first time an American president would cross the Atlantic Ocean while in office. But there was to be another first connected with this voyage — the first long-distance radio telephone was to be installed on the *Washington.*

Since the invention of the *triode* (or three-element) type of radio tube by Lee De Forest in 1907, ships at sea had been able to use radio for ship-to-ship conversation. But there was a serious limitation; beyond a distance of seventy miles the radio signals became too weak to be picked up. Bucky was given the task of helping with the installation of a revolutionary new radiotelephone system that would allow President Wilson's voice to be carried across the entire ocean. While the battleship was at anchor in the harbor of Breste, France, the President was speaking to government officials in Arlington, Virginia.

His years in the Navy were a time of intense learning for Bucky. He spent much of his spare time reading books on architecture, engineering, mathematics, aviation, industrial design, and philosophy. His brain sucked ideas up out of these books like a vacuum cleaner. And in his mind, he began to sort out those ideas which seemed especially important for man's struggle against the forces of nature. He tried to figure out the directions in which civilizations were moving. At the moment, he was unable to work out anything that made sense. Later in his life, the pattern would become clearer.

"I can see," he wrote, "how we went from the wire to the wireless, from the track to the trackless, from the visible to the invisible, where more and more could be done with less and less!"

No matter what he thought about, battleships, houses, radios, or airplanes, Bucky's mind seemed to be able to leap ahead, to think in terms of something new, something as yet undeveloped. All the seaplanes he watched

taking off used propellers to move them quickly across
the surface of the water. Why propellers? Was there a
simpler, a more efficient way of doing the same thing?

Once Bucky had set himself a problem, it held his
complete attention until he had found some kind of solution. Day and night, he thought about propellers. The
principle behind their use seemed simple enough; it was
a practical application of Newton's Third Law of Dy-
namics, which said that for every action there was an
equal and opposite reaction. The propeller pushed the
air one way, and the propeller itself moved in the opposite direction. When the push was strong enough, since
the propeller was attached to the plane she went forward
along with it.

But the pushing power of a propeller was limited. If
you wanted to lift a heavier plane off the ground, one propeller would not be enough. What was needed was a simpler method of generating greater pushing power to
overcome the inertia of the airplane. But how to do it?

The thought came in a flash. Turbines, that was it!
Turbines, the wheels with blades that were spun by the
waters of Niagara Falls to produce electricity. Why not
design a small turbine, small enough to be part of an
airplane, with blades that were turned by air? Bucky's
pencil began to draw designs on paper.

First, there had to be a way of compressing the air that
entered the front of the turbine engine. Then that compressed air had to be heated, so that it would rush
through the turbine at a high speed. Then the blades
would push the heated air out through the back of the
engine with tremendous force. Why, a turbine engine

ought to provide more than a hundred times the push of a propeller. With two such engines, one mounted on each wing, there was no telling how fast an airplane would go.

But a new thought crossed his mind. Once more, his pencil flashed over the paper, moving scarcely a moment ahead of his thought to put lines together into diagrams. With such engines you could do away with wheels and the long, rolling takeoff. The turbine engines could be mounted on swinging gimbals — the kind used to mount a ship's compass. Then, with the engines swung into a face-up position, the air would be sucked in, compressed, heated, pushed out by the turbine — and the plane would simply rise straight up in the air. Who needed wheels? Stilts would be enough. Then, once the plane was airborne and high enough, the turbines could be made to swing quickly through a ninety-degree angle, and the plane would move forward.

Bucky began to muse about the turbine airplane itself. With increased power and greater speeds, the entire airplane would have to undergo change. He took time out to read what few books and articles about aerodynamic properties were available. In one of the articles he found the answer. Raindrops!

When a drop of rain fell through the atmosphere, its normally spherical shape changed. The rubbing of the air against the drop created a teardrop design. Bucky copied the shape carefully into his notebook:

This was the shape of his airplane of the future —
streamlined. With a streamlined plane, where the resistance of the air became as small as possible, smooth flying at great speeds would be possible.

Not satisfied with his work, Bucky added some refine-
ments to his plane design. He placed little rocket engines
on each side of the plane. By shooting out jets of gas, the
turbine plane could be made even more maneuverable.
After that came another flash of genius. Why not add a
three-wheel system that could be hooked on by a simple
clutch to turn the plane into a ground taxi? Or add a
paddle-wheel system, so that you could land on water
and become a water taxi? The turbine engine opened vast
realms of opportunity for invention.

When Bucky tried to interest people in his idea, they
were polite but vague. Wouldn't that kind of engine be
rather impractical? What would be the effect of the hot
gas on the metal parts of the engine — wouldn't they
melt? How could a tiny turbine like that be efficient? It
soon became apparent that American industry was not
ready to begin even thinking about such new ideas. American industry was not ready for R. Buckminster Fuller.

Bucky didn't care. He had already made up his mind.
He would always be ten jumps ahead of the world.

EARLY PHOTOS

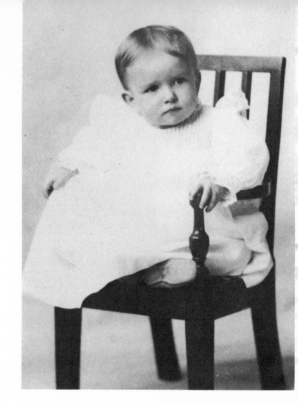

Bucky Fuller, age one-
and-a-half years

Bucky at four (front center) with his mother, brother and sister

Four-year-old Bucky
with his sister Lesley

Lesley, Grandmother Fuller and Bucky

Character sketches by an inventive eleven-year-old

The Milton Academy football team, quarterback Buckminister Fuller lower left

Bucky at Bear Island

Skipper Fuller at wheel of U.S.S. *Wego*

Bucky and Anne Hewlett ready for the Beaux Arts Ball

Above, Ensign Fuller one month before the end of World War I. At left, in whites for his wedding

3

A Year of Decision

In 1918, during the last months of the war, people in cities in the United States and soldiers in military camps began to fall sick with a disease called influenza. Up until then, only babies and very old people had been thought to be in any danger of dying from this illness. Now suddenly people of all ages began to die by the hundreds. There did not seem to be any way to stop the spread of influenza.

Doctors insisted that crowding and spitting were two ways of spreading influenza; they urged people to keep away from theaters and to wear gauze masks over their noses and mouths. There was little agreement about how to cure the disease; some doctors recommended doses of castor oil, others claimed that alcohol would do the trick, while yet others told their patients only to get plenty of fresh air.

So, some influenza victims drank whiskey and others slept with their bedroom windows wide open in spite of the chilly fall weather. But neither of these treatments seemed to make much difference. Living or dying seemed to depend more upon a person's own ability to resist the influenza attack and not upon treatment.

The disease had begun in Europe, and then had moved to the North American continent. During the years 1918 and 1919, about twenty-two million people all over the world were killed by influenza itself or by complications, such as pneumonia, brought on by the disease. Such a sickness that sweeps across wide areas of the world, as did the influenza then, is called a *pandemic* — that is, a disease which is epidemic everywhere.

The influenza pandemic reached into almost every American home. And Bucky and Anne Fuller were not spared. Their little daughter, Alexandra, was stricken with the disease. For a long time it was not certain that she would recover; then the fever broke and she became well again. But the ordeal left her a frail child, with her body easy prey to harmful microbes. Within the next three years, she caught poliomyelitis and then one of the most dreaded childhood diseases, spinal meningitis. This was all she could bear; in 1922, at the age of four, Alexandra died. Her death left Bucky depressed and despondent; he seemed unable to return to the cheerful, optimistic person he had always been.

During the years of Alexandra's illness, Bucky had moved through two different jobs. After receiving his discharge from the Navy in 1919, he had returned to the Armour Company. Remembering his past experience and excellent record, the management offered him the position of assistant export manager.

Many returning veterans of the war were not as lucky. During the months and years spent in the armed forces, their old jobs had been taken by younger men or by those

who had escaped the call to arms. Great labor strikes
were going on in many industries. Mines and factories
all over the country were shut down. Bucky knew he was
fortunate, and he enjoyed the new responsibilities at the
Armour plant. With those responsibilities went a salary
of fifty dollars a week.

Normally, such a salary would have been enough for
two young married people. But at the Fuller home, the
money had to cover more than just rent and food. Two
trained nurses were needed to take care of Alexandra.
Anne and Bucky hardly managed to keep up with their
expenses. So, when Bucky was offered a better paying
position with the Kelley-Springfield Truck Company, he
gladly accepted. But then Alexandra died; the extra
money seemed meaningless in the face of the tragedy.

That same autumn Anne's father suggested a change.
He showed Bucky a concrete block. It was about sixteen
inches long, eight inches wide, and four inches thick.
There were two cylindrical holes spaced apart and going
all the way through; this made it easy to lift the block
with one hand. What distinguished this concrete block
from building bricks was its weight — only two pounds!

Bucky was amazed and interested. He could see some
fibers embedded in the concrete and asked about them.
Mr. Hewlett explained that these were simply pieces of
straw bonded into the cement. The result was the lightest
but toughest brick possible, easy to carry and difficult to
break. This concrete brick had been invented by Mr.
Hewlett himself. The holes in the brick were an ingen-
ious addition. For an outside wall, the blocks could be

laid so that the holes made a continuous cylindrical space. Then, concrete could be poured into this space to create extra support in each brick column. The blocks without filled holes could be used to build a lighter, insulating inner wall. Thus, an architect would have a way of getting around the difficult problem of brick wall construction — the expansion and contraction of bricks with changes in temperature. Regular brick tended to crack easily unless the brick mason worked very carefully. The straw-filled bricks could be used to make inside and outside walls that were independent of one another; there would be no cracking.

Now Mr. Hewlett told Bucky what he wanted of him. A machine was needed to mold the brick efficiently for manufacture and distribution. He knew that Bucky had the imagination and inventiveness to create such machinery. He asked Bucky to leave his job with Kelley-Springfield and to become a partner with him in a corporation set up to manufacture the blocks. Bucky would be president of the corporation and would share in the patent rights and half the profits.

It was a most generous offer and Bucky could not refuse. With a grin and a handshake he accepted. And ideas began to bubble up in his mind at the very moment — ideas about how to set up the molds so that a continuous pouring process could go on, about how to mix the straw and concrete and to get the mixture poured in the fewest possible steps.

Preparations for the new company were time-consuming. Patents for new inventions had to be filed with

the government in Washington. Then, when Bucky had
worked out the details of the block-making machines,
new patents had to be filed. Mr. Hewlett and Bucky decided to call the new brick the Stockade Building Block.
The first Stockade Company factory was built in 1923 in
Summit, New Jersey.

Bucky knew little about the building business and less
about how an industrial corporation should be run. But
he was willing to learn. He set out to prove to the world
that Mr. Hewlett's invention was the most marvelous
thing that had happened in the history of house-building.

The Stockade Company prospered. More factories
were opened to meet the demand for bricks. By 1927,
Bucky had built two hundred and forty houses using the
Stockade system for the walls. And as he worked, he
learned more and more about the building industry. He
was astonished by what he saw; much of the planning
and building of houses in the United States was carried
out by methods that had not changed in hundreds of
years! Few architects and contractors seemed to understand or even know about the new technologies that could
improve the techniques of building. And what seemed
even more astounding to him was that no one in architecture or in the building industry seemed to care about
what would be happening during the following hundred
years. No one seemed to be planning for the future.

The fourth Stockade Building System plant was built
in Chicago; in 1926 Bucky and Anne moved to the great
city on the shores of Lake Michigan. The lake was a poor
substitute for the Atlantic Ocean, which Bucky missed.
But he was content to see some water; it made him happy

to stand at the lakefront of the "Windy City" and look out to the horizon, where the water and sky blended.

The following year another daughter was born to Anne and Bucky. They named her Allegra, from the Italian word meaning joyful, or happy. And the coming of Allegra was a joyful happening for the Fullers. It meant they could forget the past sadness.

But with the joy came a new blow. Mr. Hewlett lost control of the Stockade Building System. He was forced to sell his shares of stock to a large business firm, the Celotex Corporation. And the men who now controlled the brick company did not have much confidence in Bucky's ability as president. Bucky himself did not own enough of the company stock to enable him to make major decisions about policy. Celotex Corporation voted him out of office. In effect, Bucky was fired by the new management.

Bucky Fuller now found himself jobless in a city that seemed strange and hostile. He became confused. He did not know what to do next. There was a need for money to pay rent and to buy food. The Fullers had saved little of Bucky's salary. And the shock of sudden change, the sudden belief that he was hopelessly incompetent was almost too much for Bucky to bear. Without telling Anne, he began to think seriously of doing away with himself.

This year of 1927, so difficult and miserable for Buckminster Fuller, was a year of exciting changes for the civilized world.

For one, a young airmail pilot named Charles Lindbergh flew a single-engined plane across the Atlantic Ocean, from New York to Paris, without stopping. The challenge to span the ocean had been flung down in 1919, with a $25,000 prize as the lure. But all who tried had failed, until the lanky youth, son of a congressman from Minnesota, stepped into his tiny cabin plane, christened *The Spirit of Saint Louis,* and took off into a Long Island dawn. It took him over thirty-three hours to fly 3600 miles and he became a heroic figure to all the world.

Other things were happening in science. A set of ideas about the nature of time and space, labeled the General Theory of Relativity, had been proposed over twenty years before by a young German physicist named Albert Einstein. For much of that time, the difficulty in understanding what Einstein was trying to say caused many people to treat his theory as a kind of standing joke. But by 1927 it began to be apparent that Einstein's joke was no joke at all, and that relativity theory might indeed open many of the closed doors of the universe.

Other scientists were beginning to find that atoms of matter were indeed made of other tiny parts that were in constant motion, but held together by electrical forces and other forces that were unknown. One of the important particles being studied was the proton, a major constituent of the kernel, or nucleus, of an atom. More disturbing was a new theory about the nature of atoms, that the parts of atoms behaved as though their energy too was atomic in nature. The idea that energy could exist in "lumps" called *quanta* was very revolutionary and difficult to accept. For example, the quantum theory of energy predicted that particles of matter that were in very rapid motion would also behave very much like waves. This kind of prediction was not only unexpected, but also unbelievable. Yet in 1927 two scientists named Davisson and Germer, working in a Bell Telephone Company laboratory, found that the tiny particles called electrons behaved exactly like light waves.

In 1900 one hundred and sixty-two out of every thousand infants under one year of age were dying in the United States. By 1927 this rate had been diminished to sixty-nine out of every thousand. Medical research had begun to eliminate the killers of man.

In 1927 a famous journalist named Lincoln Steffens returned from the Soviet Union, heralding that new country's progress. He said that he had seen the future and that it worked. What he did not know was that a struggle for political control was going on in the Kremlin. The great Bolshevik leader, Lenin, had died in 1924. Two men with widely differing views on how to direct the economic and social progress of the new Russia were competing for his place. One was Leon Trotsky; the other, Josef Stalin. The winner was Stalin, in 1927; in that year the path that would be taken by the Soviet communistic society was decided.

In Italy, meanwhile, an elementary-school teacher named Benito Mussolini had come to political power as head of a party called *fasci di combattimento*, or "groups for combat." Their party insignia was the bundle of twigs bound about an axehead, called *fasces*, and used by the ancient Romans as a symbol of authority. Mussolini believed in a new way of governing people — by force and by deception. This new way was given a name: *fascism*.

In Germany, a disgruntled and unhappy ex-soldier

and artist named Adolf Hitler found that he had the ability to arouse and lead people. He entered German politics as the head of a new party called the National Socialists — or, for short, the Nazis. Hitler employed the same methods as Mussolini — he played upon the fears and hatreds of the Germans to win followers. But in 1927 his attempts to seize power had been repulsed. In the elections of that year, the Nazis lost most of their seats in the German Parliament, and most people felt that Adolf Hitler's career was quite finished.

As for the United States, there had been unprecedented prosperity since the silent and dour New England Republican, Calvin Coolidge, had been reelected president in 1924. His Party's slogan had been: "Keep Cool with Coolidge!" The presidential campaign was the first in which radio was used extensively as a means of reaching the public ear. One thing Coolidge did try to do was to get the nations of the world to disarm; however, the disarmament meeting he arranged ended in failure.

Private industry was earning more money than ever. By 1927 the total came to almost sixty-four billion dollars — up fifty billion from the total in 1900. The automobile had arrived as a major means of transportation; in those twenty-seven years, the output of motor vehicles had risen from four thousand per year to three and a half million.

Man's greatest dream — to fly like the birds — was also coming true. In 1927, there were already twenty-seven hundred civil airplanes in operation in the United States, with fifteen hundred pilots licensed to fly them.

But the most important change in America was in the quantity of energy available to move the levers and cogs of industrial machines. Petroleum and waterpower energy had tripled since 1900. Now a new form of energy had been made available in vast quantities: electrical energy. In 1902, what electric plants existed were turning out a bare six million kilowatt hours of electrical energy. By 1927 this amount had been multiplied almost twenty times.

It seemed to Bucky Fuller that there was no place for him in the rapidly changing world. He had taken on the responsibilities of a grown man — a wife, children, a home, and a job. But he had failed.

Or was it the other way around? Had the world failed Buckminster Fuller? Was Alexandra dead at the age of four because the world had failed in its responsibility to attack the diseases of man in a proper manner? Was his position with the Stockade Company gone because the building industry of the United States refused to move forward with changing technology?

Night after night, Bucky held these conversations with himself. Whose was the failure? Whose the blame?

One night, looking down at the black, tossing waters of Lake Michigan, he knew that he would have to come to a final decision. A bitter wind roared down the lakefront, but Bucky hardly felt the cold. He stared into the water and rearranged all the arguments in his mind. If he jumped now, Anne and Allegra would be freed from future want and suffering. Mr. Hewlett and the Fuller family would see to that.

All right, he said to himself, that much is obvious. If I go, Anne and Allegra will not suffer for want of material things. If I stay, I must stay on my own terms, and life may be difficult for them.

Did a man have the right to play God with his own life? Bucky knew that he would have to make a decision on this night, right there, looking down at the weaving, changing patterns on the water's surface.

Suddenly, in the dark, windblown night, the answer came to him. It was a simple answer, and he knew it was right. The answer was: *time to think!* A man could only know if his genius was real and worthwhile by doing nothing except thinking for a long time. This was how a great philosopher named Descartes, over three hundred years before, had given birth to his genius; he had locked himself away in a little hut for the winter with nothing but a little food, a stove, and his thoughts. This was how Henry Thoreau, the famous friend of Margaret Fuller, had found his genius — alone in the country near Walden Pond in Massachusetts.

There was no mystery, no secret. If a man felt that he possessed some kind of genius, then he needed time to think things out, no matter what the sacrifice. Bucky turned away from the lake, pulled his coat more tightly about him, and went home to tell Anne.

How would an average American housewife, at home with a newborn baby, react to her husband's coming home and saying, "Dear, I have decided that for a year or two I am not going to work. I have to use that time to think out my future, to figure out just what it is I can do for the world. I don't know how we'll live. I probably won't talk to you very much. But have faith in me, and we'll manage somehow."

This is what Bucky Fuller told his wife. He had made his decision about the future. He believed in himself and in his ability to do something important for the world. But doing it, there had to be much thinking and very little talking. He would have to cut himself off from outside influences. He had his real experiences in the Navy, in industry, and in building upon which to make his plans; not many men his age had such a valuable background.

"This may sound crazy, Anne," said Bucky, "but I feel as though I have been placed in charge of an important natural resource — myself. My head is full of ideas about how to change the world, about how to make it a better world. I have to do it my way, Anne."

Anne Hewlett Fuller looked at her husband. Her eyes told him that she loved him and that her faith in him was unshaken. That was all Bucky needed.

He found them a flat in a low-rent tenement in one of the slum areas of Chicago. First he made sure that the building was fireproof. There, he, Anne, and the baby began a hand-to-mouth existence that lasted almost two years. Somehow there was food for the family; somehow there was clothing for Allegra. Bucky had made many friends in Chicago. Though he came from a blueblood Boston family, he was no snob; his friends came from all walks of life. One friend was the man who lived in the next apartment. He was a kind fellow who always

helped Anne carry the garbage from her kitchen to the
hall incinerator. When he bent over, Anne could see the
butt end of a revolver poking out of his shoulder holster.
He was a gunman who worked for Al Capone, the crim-
inal king of Chicago's gangs. But to Anne he was a kind
neighbor who was Bucky's friend, and who wanted to
help.

During those two years, while his family was supported by the Hewletts and the Fullers and by his Chicago friends, Bucky began to invent things for the world
of the future. His Navy experience had taught him that a
ship was a self-contained, floating city that was at the
mercy of nature. On board a ship, man learned quickly
to cope with the unknown. New ideas and inventions that
resulted from need were quickly put to use on ships. This
was even more true in the case of the radio; the time lag
between new inventions and their application was very
short. Radio techniques were changing every day. And in
the realm of flying, new inventions were tried out almost
as soon as they appeared. In these areas, Bucky saw,
progress in technology was causing almost instant change.

Where was the lag between invention and application
the greatest? Bucky realized that it was in the building
industry. Look how that industry had failed to take advantage of Mr. Hewlett's invention. Man had hardly
changed the type of shelter he had been building for
himself in the past hundred years. Houses were still
heavy, squarish masses that, once put down, could not be
moved. They were still not being built to resist the stronger forces in nature; earthquakes, floods, and hurri-
canes. The use of materials in house-building was terribly

inefficient; there was much needless waste. Yet contractors and trade unions alike resisted the coming of new technological ideas, for fear of losing profits and jobs. Here was where inventiveness was needed the most. Here was where new ideas in science and technology could create the most needed changes.

Bucky saw that the new world, this world of 1927 about him, was a world of *motion*. More and more, man was on the move: first ships, then trains, then automobiles, and now airplanes. He realized that he would have to find a way to adapt to such an increasingly mobile world. The job that the universe had in mind for Buckminster Fuller was not to change man; it was to change man's surroundings.

4

The Birth of DYMAXION

ONCE he had decided to remain alive, Buckminster Fuller began to prepare for his self-appointed task in earnest. He spent hours reading in libraries. What were the newest advances in scientific thinking? What was the impact of this thinking on invention and industry? How much were industries in the United States and all over the world producing? Bucky sought the answers to these questions and more. Along with his reading went more hours of solitary thinking.

He realized that the new concepts in physics and chemistry, the new ideas about how nature worked, formed the real basis for change and invention in the world of machines. And the world of machines was the world of large-scale industry and manufacturing. There the old problems of production were being solved by new, efficient methods such as the moving assembly line. Workers in a factory did not have to rush from one corner to another to put together the different parts of an automobile; the auto was assembled as it moved from place to place along a line of workers, each of whom stayed in his place.

The one problem to which this new kind of industrial efficiency had not been applied was that of building shelters for human beings. The planning and construction of individual houses consisted of a series of slow, awkward, and very expensive operations. An architect generally tried to design each of his houses to be quite different from the next. Contractors were still using building techniques that had not changed in hundreds, even thousands, of years.

Why didn't architects and builders think in terms of assembling houses like automobiles or airplanes?

Bucky decided that the shelter industry was prevented from making such a change by the complicated network that had been woven through the ages between banker, builder, and occupant when a house was built. Houses cost so much that the individual house buyer could not afford to pay the entire cost at once. A buyer had to go to the bank for a loan; the banker called this a mortgage, and arranged for the buyer to pay off his mortgage in small parts, like a monthly rent. Of course, these small payments included not only part of the actual cost of the house, but also interest on the loan. Over a period of years, while the mortgage was being paid off, a house buyer would be paying thousands of dollars extra to the banker. Any kind of planning that would make houses inexpensive might break down this loan system.

Another problem was that of the actual weight of materials that went into building a house. When Bucky asked architects how much their houses weighed, they regarded him as though he were mad, shrugged, and went away. Who cared how much a house weighed? After all, it just sat there on the earth. The earth was certainly strong enough to support the heaviest house man could produce! Bucky was reminded of the reaction of his math teacher at Milton Academy to his question about the weight of a cube.

Why should houses have to be heavy, cubic objects bound to the surface of the earth by the weight of their materials?

Why couldn't a house be made of some material that was as strong as steel or concrete, yet much lighter? Why couldn't a house be strong enough to withstand the buffeting of winds or storms, yet be as light as an airplane?

Bucky thought about the new kind of aircraft called *zeppelins* (after their inventor, Count Zeppelin of Germany) that had been developed during the First World War. In America, they were called *dirigibles*. These aircraft were rigid, lighter-than-air, and shaped like a cigar. A zeppelin had a framework of light girders filled with gasbags, and covered with a cloth skin. The gasbags were filled with enough hydrogen gas to lift the zeppelin up through the air. Power to move forward was supplied by gasoline engines that turned propellers. At that very moment, in 1927, the Germans were building the largest dirigible of all time, the *Graf Zeppelin*, eight hundred feet long and one hundred feet across. The *Graf* was designed to carry fifty passengers and their baggage, plus the crew, across the Atlantic Ocean. As a matter of fact, it was designed to be able to fly completely around the world.

But what was a dirigible? Why, it was really a long, floatable house. And like a ship at sea, this floating house was self-sufficient; its power and disposal units were all built-in. Slowly, the plan for a light, movable house began to form in Bucky's mind. Tip the dirigible up; then, divide the long cylinder into sections, each section a floor, or deck, of the house.

He began to scribble designs on a pad of paper. First, each upright section would be a hexagon:

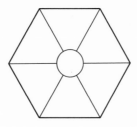

Then, the hexagons could be piled up, one atop the other, hanging from a strong, central mast:

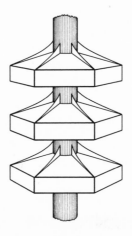

In a conventional house the parts were supported by
the combined forces of an upper part pushing downward
(like a brick in a wall) and a lower part pushing back up
(the brick beneath). Architects called this kind of pushing *compression*. Thus the walls of a house stayed up because of the compression of their parts. If a different
force (for example, an earthquake) moved part of the
wall sideways, compression made the house fall down.

But a dirigible was built in a different way. The metal
spars were tied together, so that they *pulled* against one
another in places. This kind of pulling was called *tension*. In a dirigible, certain parts were pushed together,
or compressed, and other parts were stressed to support
each other by pulling, or tension. Strong metal cables
could be tensed to support tremendous weights or forces,
much greater than what could be supported by typical
house walls.

Were there metals strong enough to support his dirigible house? Bucky read through the latest publications
of metals research scientists. He found that metallurgists
in the airplane industry were on the track of new combinations of metals, called *alloys*, that might result eventually in the production of materials of tremendous
strength.

It was true that steel was strong, but it was heavy.
What Bucky wanted was the lightest possible material
that could support the greatest possible weight. The success of his ideas would be based upon *using the least to
accomplish the most*. Bucky found the one word that expressed what he expected technological research to do
for the housing industry.

That word was *synergy*.

Synergy was a word that you might not find in every-day conversation, but it was a word well-known to chemists. It meant the behavior of a whole system that could not be predicted by the behavior of any of its individual parts. For example, chemists knew that there were two chemical elements, sodium and chlorine, that differed not only in their appearance, but also in their individual behavior. Sodium was a soft, silvery metal that burst into flame the moment it touched water. It certainly could not be eaten without burning and poisoning the eater. Chlorine, on the other hand, was a heavy, greenish gas, also very poisonous to man. But if these two elements were allowed to come together and react, the result was a white-appearing crystalline substance called sodium chloride. And this stuff was far from poisonous; it sat on the tables of most American families in saltshakers! Thus, the whole system called sodium chloride had neither the appearance nor properties of its two individual components.

Bucky saw that man had to begin thinking in terms of synergy; that is, if man wanted to use science and technology to the best advantage. It was not the individual parts of nature that were necessarily most important; it was the *integrated behaviors* of these parts. He realized that there were many blessings of synergy waiting to be discovered: new metal alloys which could lead to the manufacture of new machines and engines; new ways of using radio waves and radio circuits. Why couldn't light energy be changed into electrical energy that could be used to open doors or control machinery?

There was plenty of useful energy in the universe, energy that existed in many different forms. When you rubbed your hand against a table, your hand became warm; that was mechanical energy being changed into heat energy. Growing plants were always changing the sun's radiant energy into the chemical energy of growth. In radio stations, sound energy was being changed first into electrical energy and then into electromagnetic energy. Radios that caught that electromagnetic energy in their antennas simply reversed the energy transformation.

The more Bucky thought about changing light energy into electrical energy that could be made to do mechanical work, the better the idea seemed. Was it possible? He dashed off a letter to his brother, Wolcott, who was working as an engineer for the General Electric Company. Did they manufacture any kind of radio tube that was sensitive to light? Could such a tube be hooked up to an electromagnetic relay that would activate switches?

Wolcott's return letter was devastating. There was no such tube. And with great humor, Wolcott had concluded his letter with, "Bucky, I love you dearly. But can't you make it easier for your relatives and friends by not including preposterous ideas?"

Bucky received somewhat the same reception when he went to a company that manufactured aluminum metal for industry. He questioned the engineers about the possibility of a strong aluminum alloy that could be used as a framework for houses. He wanted to use such an alloy in his dirigible house.

But the engineers shook their heads. Strong aluminum

alloys to be used in house-building? It was a preposterous idea! Aluminum was good for making coffeepots and souvenirs. It was a soft metal, and would always be used only where soft metals were useful. When Bucky began to talk to them about synergy and the chances of finding his alloys, the engineers became coldly polite and said good-bye.

Bucky was undismayed by such failures.

He kept planning his dirigible house. The decks would be held in place by tension cables, yet the whole house would be light enough to be lifted up and moved by a zeppelin. After all, the rapid progress of aviation was bound to change man from a stationary, root-putting-down condition to a mobile, "to-ing and fro-ing" state. If the airplane was shrinking the earth in size year by year, then a man should not have to be bound to a specific stationary dwelling in a specific place.

What man needed was a home that could be transported by air and put down anywhere on earth, at the North Pole or in the Sahara Desert. Such a house would have to be self-sufficient, carrying its own power, water (which would be reusable), and disposal units. Bucky thought of the earth as the "Air Ocean World," where air travel could make it possible for man to locate himself in places that had always been considered inaccessible. Synergetic discoveries would provide ways for man to control hostile environments that were too cold, too hot, or too stormy. It was time to begin thinking of a universal shelter that could be used by anyone anywhere.

Of course, the kind of conventional house designed by architects could not be moved at all, or at least not without

great difficulty. That kind of house was far too heavy. But
a dirigible house, lightweight and mass-produced like an
airplane, was another matter. Bucky sketched out a
twelve-deck house, hung by tension cables on a central
hollow mast. The top of this mast could be hooked onto
the nose of a dirigible and carried away. It would take
only one day to produce such a house, since the parts
would be prefabricated and interlocking.

Bucky's imagination soared further. A dirigible could
carry the finished house to any spot on the face of the
earth. First, a small dynamite bomb could be dropped to
make a hole in the ground. Then, the lower part of the
mast could be lowered into the hole. Finally, cement
would be poured around the mast to form a solid supporting base. The dirigible house was planned to have its
own electric power plant, heating system, and sewage
disposal all built-in. There would be no necessity to tie
into existing city electrical and sewage systems. In order
to make the transportation of his house more efficient,
Bucky designed a streamlined plastic shield to be placed
about the house. The shape of the shield was the same
that he had designed for his jet plane during his Navy
days.

Bucky even figured out the cost for his twelve-story
tower house. Once mass production had been achieved, it
would be possible to sell and deliver such a house for
only $10,000. This was a fraction of the cost of a conven-
tional house with the same features. Bucky's house had
such luxuries as a gymnasium and swimming pool all
built in. However, when he showed his design to architects, they told him that he was a wild, impractical

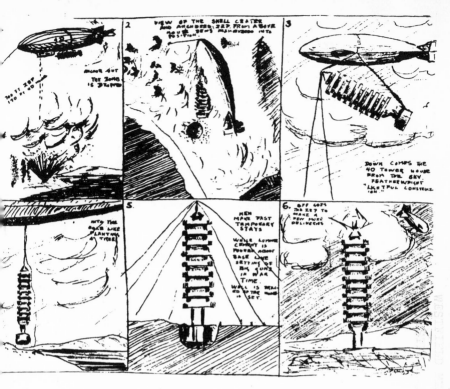

Sketches of dirigible transporting a ten-decker

dreamer. In fact, most of them resented the nerve of this young upstart who dared to design houses without having ever attended a school of architecture.

But the dirigible house was only a beginning for Bucky, a kind of mental practice that laid the groundwork for more practical thinking about shelters. His fantastic, twelve-deck house became a single-floor dwelling that could be turned out easily on an industrial assembly line.

Bucky called this plan the *4-D*, or fourth dimension, house. With this name, he was paying homage to Einstein's theory of relativity. When we want to locate a point in space, we have to measure from some beginning point in three directions that are at right angles to each other. To these three *dimensions* of measuring, Einstein had added a fourth: *time.* Thus, 4-D represented the time dimension, the *new* dimension.

Bucky worked out the details of his 4-D house with painstaking precision. He dreamed up things that had never been heard of by the housing industry. In the first place, the house had no windows! Instead, the walls themselves were made of glass — two plates of glass with a vacuum in between for each wall. This kind of construction would insulate the house more efficiently than ordinary insulating material, so that the house would be warm in winter and cool in summer. Of course, such glass walls had not yet been invented.

In order to insure privacy, Bucky's house was fitted with shutters that could roll down over the walls at the touch of a switch. Space inside the house was simply divided in terms of the equilateral triangles that made up the whole hexagon floor plan. Two of the triangles served as bedrooms, one for the kitchen and utility room, one for the library and study, and the final two could be combined into a diamond, or rhomboid, shape to be a large, comfortable living room. Each bedroom had its own bathroom attached, and here Bucky had worked out a very unusual system.

The bathroom fixtures were made to be independent of city water and sewage systems, since this was to be a house that could be erected anywhere in the world at a moment's notice. It took only a quart of water for the complete operation of a bathroom! The shower was what Bucky called his "fog gun." During his Navy experience, he had learned that a man could come up on deck from the engine room with his face all dirty and grimy, and just by standing watch in a fog that face would become as clean as a whistle. There was something about the way that fog particles struck while the ship was in motion that made the fog act like a combination shower and scrubbing brush. A compressor, then, could be used to spray the water out like a fog in Bucky's shower compartment. Then, the used water could be collected, filtered clean, returned to a storage tank, and be used again.

As for the other parts of the bathroom, wastes could be packaged and disposed of by chemical means. An exhaust fan removed unpleasant odors. In short, Bucky was taking advantage of scientific and technical knowledge to design ways of washing and heating the human body as efficiently as possible. The 4-D house made his point clear. A shelter for man had to make him able to cope with his natural environment as easily as possible.

There was no wasted space in Bucky's house. The different living areas were separated by partitions which were actually movable shelves, hangers, or laundry units that went from floor to ceiling. Doors between these areas were actually curtains that could be opened or closed by compressed air controls. All the dusting in the house was done mechanically by compressed air and vacuum systems.

He figured out the cost of such a house in terms of being able to manufacture it on a factory assembly line. The weight of the entire house came to 6000 pounds. From the cost of materials and labor, Bucky arrived at a sales price of twenty-five cents per pound. If it had been possible to produce a 4-D house right there and then, it would have cost a home buyer only $1,500! Bucky visualized the parts of his house being turned out by the thousands. The 4-D house would be a new kind of machine that would help break the chains that had bound homeowners to specific communities. He made up a new name for those people who would be living in portable, independent, 4-D homes everywhere in the future: a *world citizenry.*

Across the ocean, in Europe, a group of young architects, led by a man named Walter Gropius, had begun a new movement in architecture called the *Bauhaus.* These people began to create new house designs based upon simplicity and streamlining. They used concrete in new ways to make wall shapes that were excitingly different from what had been done before.

Bucky had read about the Bauhaus school of architecture, and he admired their decision to revolt against old-fashioned techniques of designing houses. But he decided that they had not gone far enough in making changes. Their houses were startlingly different in artistic style; but they still used steel girders within the brick and cement walls for support. The Bauhaus architects did not plan their houses in terms of the revolutionary progress that was going on in science and technology. They did not think in terms of the industrialization of house-building in the same way Bucky did. The new homes they designed were still individually different, and they were expensive to build.

For Bucky, the Bauhaus movement did not mean real

progress in housing; he saw the movement as a kind of popular and appealing fad of the moment. Their houses were the same heavy cubes; after all, not even the new young architects cared about how much a house weighed. And like houses of old, their houses had to be tied to city power lines and sewers. Their houses could not be lifted and moved about easily. In short, while new ideas about the planning and building of houses were emerging, the 4-D house was really the only one that had been designed to house all people everywhere at minimum cost. And it was the only house that had built into it materials and devices that had not yet been invented!

Then Bucky's prediction of things to come began to come true. Many of the materials he had imagined, the nonexistent ones, were slowly beginning to be found in research laboratories. Even his dream of a door you could open without touching a doorknob came true in 1928. He received a telegram from his brother Wolcott: YOU CAN NOW OPEN YOUR DOOR BY WAVING YOUR HAND AFTER ALL STOP WE HAVE DEVELOPED PHOTOELECTRIC CELL AND RELAY STOP SEVENTY TWO DOLLARS FOR THE SET.

Bucky managed to borrow materials and money enough to make a scale model of the 4-D house. The different parts were fashioned exactly as they would have been made in a factory for assembly. The model was about three feet across. Through the double glass walls you could see miniature furniture in the rooms. In the living room, Bucky placed on a miniature sofa a little doll that had no clothes.

"Oh, Bucky!" cried Anne when she saw the doll.

"What will people think? Are you trying to shock them?"

"No, no," laughed Bucky. "The point I want the doll to make is that the Fuller 4-D house makes it possible to control temperature and humidity. My house can be so warm and comfortable, the people inside won't even have to wear clothing for protection."

"Hmmm," muttered Anne to herself. "I hope everyone understands that!"

In May of 1928, Bucky decided to bring his house to the attention of American architects in a dramatic way. He asked Anne's father, Mr. Hewlett, to tell the American Institute of Architects that he, R. Buckminster Fuller, was prepared to assign to the Institute full rights to all patents for the 4-D house.

Bucky had taken the precaution of patenting all of his 4-D plans; his experience with the patents for the Hewlett concrete brick had taught him how to do this. Anne's father was now vice-president of the Institute, which was the most prominent professional organization in the architectural field. But Mr. Hewlett cautioned Bucky not to expect too much. "I'll be glad to do what you ask, but architects are a very conservative group. I don't know how they will will respond."

What they said in very blunt fashion was no. In fact, the Institute members were so outraged by Bucky's offer that they passed a resolution saying, ". . . the American Institute of Architects is opposed to any kind of house designs that are to be manufactured alike as peas-in-a-pod!"

And then recognition came in a different way. The art editor of a Chicago newspaper, the *Evening Post*, heard about the 4-D house. He came to see it, was impressed by Bucky's vision, and wrote a feature article that the *Post* printed. Some months later Bucky received a call from the publicity department of one of the most famous department stores in the world, Marshall Field and Company in Chicago.

"Mr. Fuller, we'd like to display your modern house in our furniture department. We have purchased a shipment of the latest designs in modern furniture from Paris. We think your model is just the thing to set that furniture off."

Delighted that someone had taken notice of his work at last, Bucky agreed. In a few days, he received a visit from one of the advertising specialists.

"Mr. Fuller, your house is a marvelous invention! But I must admit that as an advertising man I am not happy about the name. 4-D . . . 4-D . . . why, that could mean anything from a failing mark in the fourth grade to a four-story apartment house. It won't do. We'll have to think of something else."

Bucky was dismayed. "But that's the whole point. 4-D stands for the fourth dimension — the one in Einstein's theory!"

The man shook his head. "Not many Americans will understand that." He seemed to notice Bucky's discomfort and changed the subject. "Look here, I have an idea. Why don't you just talk to me about your house — what it means to you, what it stands for. Now I'll just listen and write down what I think are key words. Perhaps we'll find something."

Bucky began to talk, while the advertising man scribbled notes. Finally, he interrupted Bucky in the middle of a sentence.

"Look here, Mr. Fuller, your talk is full of scientific terms. But I notice that there are some words that turn up over and over. Here are three of them: *dynamic, maximum, ion*. I know what the first two mean, but what's an ion?"

"That's an atom that has gained or lost electrons and has become an electrically charged particle."

"Hmm, ion — well, that's scientific enough. What if I put together the first syllables of dynamic and maximum, and then add ion. Dy-max-ion — by golly, that's it!" He pounded a fist into his other hand in excitement. "There's the name for your modern house — the Dymaxion House!"

Bucky's eyes gleamed behind his thick glasses. He tasted the word on his tongue. It had a fine futuristic sound. *Dymaxion*. He shook his head vigorously up and down, saying yes. It was a perfect name.

The pleased advertising specialist shook Bucky's hand. "It's your word, Mr. Fuller. I'll see that Marshall Field and Company patents it in your name."

A warm glow spread through Bucky's body. Finding the new name was a good omen. He did not yet know that all his future work would be stamped with the Buckminster Fuller trademark — DYMAXION.

5

Great Ideas, but Bad Luck

DESPITE the exhibition of the Dymaxion House model in the great Chicago department store, there were few architects or builders who expressed interest in that new design for the future.

The year was 1929. Bucky decided that two years in Chicago were enough; it was time to depart. Carrying Allegra and a large supply of diapers, he and Anne boarded the train going east. It was summer, and the natural place to go was to The Big House on Bear Island.

Standing on the rocky beach with Allegra in his arms, Bucky felt he had come home. The wind flung salt spray in his face. Overhead sea gulls turned and drifted on outspread, white wings. He carefully put Allegra down on the beach. While she picked up and threw little stones, laughing to see them bounce, Bucky put on the old tennis shoes that would protect his feet from the sharp spines of sea urchins on the ocean floor. Then, he picked up his daughter and dashed into the sea.

Penobscot Bay waters were ice-cube cold; but Bucky had found a way to have cold-water fun. His method consisted of rushing in up to his chest and falling forward

with a great splash. A moment later he would dash back
to the beach, warm up in the sun, and then back into the
water. Allegra loved to be part of this game. She did not
seem to mind the cold, and greeted each rush to the sea
with screams of joy.

All too soon the summer was over. It was time to secure the Island for the winter and leave. Bucky decided
that he would settle his family in New York City. But
where? Anne's father came to the rescue; he invited them
to live on the Hewlett estate on Long Island. Bucky accepted at once. He knew that in the home where she had
grown up Anne would feel secure and happy. But he had
no thoughts for his own security and happiness. He cared
only about his ideas for changing the world; day and
night, these thoughts boiled about in his mind.

The early fall of 1929 seemed a happy time for
Americans. There were jobs for almost everyone who
wanted to work. More men acquired riches than ever before. Business was good; factories all over the country
were turning out hundreds of different products for people to buy.

It was true that some people were not sharing in this
prosperity, mainly farmers, coal miners, and textile
workers. But the general increase in the profits of large
business organizations and in the wages of workers
caused a kind of craziness in people. Everyone seemed to
feel that it was easy to become rich. Moreover, it became
easier for a person to get things without spending money.
Almost everything for sale, from a fur coat to a house,
could be bought on credit — a small payment at first,
and then a few dollars a week for a year or years.

And the average American had found a new money game to play, a game called buying and selling common stocks in the stock market. Before this, for most people, the stock market had been a kind of mysterious operation in which only rich businessmen took part. Actually, it was not so mysterious. In order to acquire cash to carry on or expand its business, a corporation could issue shares of common stock to be made available for sale to the public. At the New York Stock Exchange, trading for the stock would go on every day. If a certain stock seemed attractive to buyers, active trading would send the price per share of stock up. But if too many shareholders decided to sell their shares, the price would fall. So, the daily price of any stock depended upon the number of shares available and the demand for those shares.

During the prosperous months of 1929, more and more people began to buy stocks on speculation; that is, in hopes that the price of the purchased stock would increase very quickly. Then the shares could be sold at a large profit. Some people were lucky; shoeshine boys were able to buy expensive cars, and factory girls wore costly mink coats. Many people withdrew their life's savings from banks and invested the money in stocks; often the same people borrowed more money from their banks to buy more shares. While some were satisfied to sell at a fair profit, most people were dazzled by the money they seemed to be making "on paper" — that is, while they were still holding on to their stocks. The craze for speculating in stocks was so widespread and great that even bankers, who ordinarily never took such risks, were urging their customers to take a chance in the stock market. And in that market, the prices of stocks rose to fantastic highs.

There were some warning signals for those who had sense enough to see them. This state of affairs could not last. Unemployment was slowly increasing, because the growing use of new machines in factories was putting people out of jobs. Business slowed down, and it began to be evident that products were being created for people who could not afford to buy things any more.

On a never-to-be-forgotten day in October, the 25th, the high prices of most stocks began a downward slide that could not be stopped. Thousands of desperate investors, trying to save whatever money they could, dumped over sixteen million shares for sale on the market. For once, there were far more sellers of stock than buyers. The usual excitement of daily trading on the floor of the Stock Exchange gave way to panic, as only selling orders flooded in.

So began the period in American history known as the Great Depression. Factories dismissed their employees and closed their doors. Rich men became paupers overnight. Millions of people lost their jobs; thousands were homeless. Neither businessmen nor the heads of government could find a ready way to return to the prosperity that had existed before the market crash. Into the years 1930 and 1931, the downward slide of American business continued. People had to live on meager savings. There were not enough salaried jobs to go around.

It was in 1930 that Bucky decided to move his family from the Hewlett house right into the heart of New York. He found a small apartment in that section of lower

Manhattan known as Greenwich Village. In those days, the Village was filled with struggling young artists and writers, most of them living on very little money. When they were not painting or sculpting or writing, they loved most of all to meet in small groups and talk. It did not take Bucky Fuller, a great lover of conversation, long to discover such a group of companions.

Most evenings would find him home or at a small cafe called *Romany Marie's,* discussing architecture, art, the Depression, and all about life in general with his friends. There were two whose friendship he valued very much: a writer name Christopher Morley, whose books had already brought him fame, and a young sculptor, Isamu Noguchi, whose superb talent had not yet been recognized.

Besides drinking and talking with his friends, Bucky spent the days writing down his ideas about city planning and house designing and spreading these ideas about town. He talked to any architect who would listen about his Dymaxion House. Some expressed excited interest, others declared the Dymaxion principle to be utter nonsense. Most simply couldn't have cared less. These indifferent people infuriated Bucky the most. After futile efforts to impress them, he would stomp away feeling like one of the prophets of the Bible disdained by his own people. Many architects felt that since he was not a graduate of a school of architecture, he had no right to tell them anything about design. But Bucky did not let their snobbishness stop him. He went right on talking to anyone who would listen about how man ought to plan for his future.

There were many days when Bucky forgot to eat and many nights when he worked on without sleep. He drank more than was good for him and smoked cigarettes incessantly. Anne worried about him terribly. But she understood the fire that burned inside him, and she did not stand in his way. Somehow, Bucky's physical strength pulled him through and made him able to carry on his work.

As time went on, Bucky began to find more and more people who took his ideas seriously. Many of these were scientists and engineers who were members of a group called *technocrats*. They believed that the Depression had been caused by the misuse of modern technology, that machines had been used to overproduce too many things that then could not be sold. Moreover, no provisions had been made for the workers who were being replaced by machines.

The theory of technocracy called for complete industrial planning for the future, along with government control of such planning. A leading technocrat had worked out a comparison of all the countries in the world based upon the amount of energy available for industrial use; by this he meant such energy as waterpower, coal, petroleum, electric power, and human muscle power. The kinds of energy available to different nations was not always the kind of energy they actually put to use. The so-called *backward* nations of the world used more human muscle power than electric power. So, the clue to easing much of the world's misery lay in the proper development of energy sources all over the world. And just as the technocrats were concerned about the proper uses of energy, Bucky became more and more concerned with the proper uses of scientific principles in architecture.

He seemed to become involved in a dozen different activities at one time. He cashed in his Navy life insurance policy in order to finance a magazine in which his ideas could be published. The name of the magazine was *Shelter*, and in the year or so it survived, Bucky tried to show that home building in the United States was a disorganized kind of industry, dominated by the desires of various manufacturing interests. The lumber people tried to persuade builders to erect wooden homes, the cement manufacturers plumped for all-cement houses, and the steel makers, of course, wanted all building to be done with steel. The architects were equally guilty of holding back progress in housing. They were tied to ideas that were a hundred years old, and had refused to accommodate themselves to the new world of science and technology. What was the future in housing? Bucky had the answer to that question: the Dymaxion House, the House of the Future.

With a few friends who understood the nature of his message, Bucky formed a group called the Structural Study Associates, or SSA. This group met formally to discuss the merging of science and architecture. They agreed that any inventions resulting from their discussions should be patented in the name of the group.

The general reaction to Bucky's articles on the scientific approach to architecture and house-building was easy to predict. Young architects who were nobodies (and often jobless) were fascinated. Older architects who were influential found, in general, that Bucky's writ-

ings seemed to be nonsensical gibberish. They wrote letters to *Shelter* complaining about the language Bucky
used to explain his ideas: "What in the devil does 'radi-
onic-time-growth-factor composition' mean?" "Can anyone tell me what is the angular modulus of unification?"
"Does Mr. Fuller really understand what Mr. Fuller is
saying?"

And one famous architect summed up his opinion of
Buckminster Fuller by writing simply, "Mechanical
civilization is spinach!"

The years of 1932 and 1933 were the worst years of
the Great Depression. The value of the dollar had been
deflated to the point where the actual buying power of a
single cent was tremendous. Bernarr McFadden, a physical health enthusiast and publisher of many magazines,
opened a chain of One Cent Restaurants in New York
City. The menu was a poor man's dream come true:

Split Pea Soup	1¢
Vegetable Stew	2¢
Beef Meatcakes	2 for 5¢
Rice & Raisin Pudding	2¢
Whole Wheat Apple Pie	2¢
Coffee . . . . 1¢ Sweet Milk	2¢
Cream for Coffee	1¢
Sugar for Coffee	1¢

Homeless men and women were sleeping in the public
parks of all the large cities. Many of the men were veterans of World War I who had lost their jobs, and who had
left their families to come to the cities in a desperate
search for work, any kind of work. In New York City, the

homeless were everywhere to be seen. Many of them were people whose houses and farms had been lost because there had been no money to pay off the mortgages. Bucky was horrified by the stories of families being cast out of their homes by ruthless sheriffs who complained that they were only doing their jobs. Scornfully, he wrote in *Shelter*:

> *Dear Hungry Mother,*
> *Weep no more,*
> *The kindly Sheriff's*
> *At the door. . . .*

In New York City, Bucky began to organize a way of providing temporary shelter for homeless men. He discovered that there were many unoccupied tenement houses and office buildings that had simply been closed and boarded up by the banks who held mortgages on them. Why should houses be sitting empty, when there were people sleeping in the streets? Bucky's plan was to fix up a group of deserted tenements on New York's East Side to provide shelter for at least 10,000 veterans during the approaching winter.

Bucky spent many hours running about, getting various companies to donate wood, plaster, and other materials to the project. Then, he rounded up a group of unemployed men who were more than willing to work for their shelter. He received permission from the bank owners of one of the old, unused houses to go in and make repairs. Under Bucky's active direction, the men were inspired to work like demons. In a few days, one floor of the old, dirty and decaying tenement was transformed into a new, clean dormitory where forty men would be able to eat and sleep in comfort.

But just as the work was finished, Bucky was informed that the men would not be allowed to sleep in the building. The companies that held insurance policies on the building had declared that there was a fire hazard in having so many people on one floor. Bucky was furious, but there was no way to change the minds of the adamant officials. His project had been made to fail. His veterans went back to sleeping in the streets and subways of New York.

Then, in the midst of failure came a stroke of luck. One of Bucky's friends and admirers, a businessman who had managed to keep his head and his money during the market crash, offered Bucky a few thousand dollars to be invested in any of the Dymaxion ideas.

In a flash Buckminster Fuller was changed from pauper to millionaire. But what to do with the money?

His head was full of plans. Could he begin to manufacture the 4-D house? No, that would take more than a million dollars to begin. What then?

One of the designs upon which Bucky had been working was called the Dymaxion Transport, an outgrowth of his original idea for a turbine jet airplane. He had conceived the plane as having two turbine engines mounted on gimbals in the wings. Because of the gimbals, the engines could be tilted at any angle, and their power could be utilized to lift the plane up, as well as to drive it forward. His imagined airplane was meant to be as versatile as a bird, to drive along the road as an auto and then leap upward into flight.

Bucky's first thought was to use the sudden wealth he had acquired to develop this airplane. But he knew that the metal alloys needed to resist the heat of the jet engines had not yet been developed. Then, the thought came to him.

Why not develop the *body* of the jet airplane as a *streamlined automobile?*

The automobiles that were being built and sold in 1933 had bodies that were just boxes on wheels. No one thought or cared about the problem of air resistance at high speeds. Bucky knew that the air resistance of a moving object increased as the *square* of the speed; that is, if the speed of a car was tripled, the air resistance would be nine times greater. At 25 miles an hour, the problem of overcoming air resistance to a car's motion was not very important. But the closer you came to 60 miles an hour, the more the power of the car's engine was wasted in pushing the atmosphere apart. Past 60 miles an hour, air resistance became a tremendous opposing force.

It was the teardrop concept that Bucky had in mind. Instead of the typical shape of an auto in the streets:

the shape that Bucky began to sketch in his notebook was more like this:

After making inquiries, Bucky discovered that he could rent one of the machine-shop buildings of the Locomobile Company in Bridgeport, Connecticut, very cheaply. This building had been standing idle for some time; the Locomobile Company was one of the many automobile companies that had failed after the stock market crash. The gift money was enough to cover not only the rent of the building, but also the hiring of skilled mechanics and engineers to work on the car. The city of Bridgeport was full of such men who had been out of work for a year or more, and Bucky soon had a competent crew working in his factory.

Now for the first time Bucky felt the thrill of actual accomplishment. He was really going to build the first Dymaxion automobile! He invited one of the most famous aeronautical engineers in the world, Starling Burgess, to take charge of the enterprise. At first, Burgess was wary. But one look at the plans for the Dymaxion Car of the future convinced him, and he accepted. In short order, pulleys and belts began to hum and whirl. Draftsmen bent over their drawing tables, intent on turning out scale diagrams of various parts of the car.

While the car was being assembled, Burgess, who had also achieved fame as a naval architect, kept Bucky busy on another project. It seemed that Burgess had promised someone else that he would build a racing sloop by July of that year. In order to get Burgess to work with him, Bucky had to agree to work on the sloop himself. Of course, Bucky knew enough about boats to do a competent job. And the two timetables coincided perfectly. When the first Dymaxion car rolled out of the factory on July 12, 1933, for its road test, the racing sloop was ready to be shipped to its owner.

Imagine an automobile shaped like the front end of a sleek, modern jet airliner! Imagine an automobile that ran on three wheels, two in the front and one in the rear! Imagine a fat automobile with windows that went all the way around, and that could hold ten people and a driver comfortably! Imagine an automobile that could be rotated in a complete circle about its tail wheel! That was Bucky's Dymaxion Car.

Using an ordinary, stock V-8 engine purchased from the Ford factory, the Dymaxion Car reached speeds up to 120 miles an hour without difficulty. It would have taken an engine with more than three times that horsepower to accomplish the same feat with any other 1933 car! And what maneuverability the Dymaxion had! It was over nineteen feet long (a good four feet longer than a Ford), but it could be parked in a much shorter curb space than the average car. All you had to do with the Dymaxion Car was to head directly into the curb, and then roll the tail section in sideways on the single wheel. When Bucky did this one day in midtown Manhattan, he stopped traffic with the crowd that collected to watch.

Bucky felt it in his bones; finally he had achieved success. He had been able to make a part of the future world believable to the world of the present. He had no doubts about this, and many agreed with him. The Dymaxion Car would push every other existing car model back into ancient history.

One of the greatest reactions to the unveiling of the

Dymaxion Car came from overseas. A group of Englishmen, interested in autos in general, wrote to ask Bucky to make a second Dymaxion Car that could be exhibited in England. And the group asked if they could send a representative to test-drive the first Dymaxion Car in the United States.

Bucky agreed with excited pleasure. Reactions to the Dymaxion Car on every side had been more than enthusiastic. An Englishman named Colonel William Forbes-Sempill cabled that he would be crossing the Atlantic on the famous dirigible, the *Graf Zeppelin.* Unfortunately, the *Graf* was not going to land in New York as usual, but would be going on to Chicago, where the 1933 World's Fair had opened. Could the Dymaxion Car be taken to that city?

The first car had already been sold to a well-known American aviator, Captain Alford Williams. At Bucky's request, Williams had a racing driver named Turner drive the car from Pittsburgh to Chicago.

The English colonel was delighted with the performance of the Dymaxion Car. He was sure that his group would want to order one. After he finished examining the car, he asked Turner to drive him in it to the Chicago airport, where he was to catch the plane to Akron, Ohio. The *Graf Zeppelin* was waiting for him at the large American dirigible base there.

Once again on the threshold of success, Bucky suffered a cruel defeat. On the way to the airport, a car driven by a petty official in the Chicago city government crashed into the Dymaxion Car. Both Turner and the other driver were killed, and the English visitor was badly injured.

Police acted quickly to remove the official's car from the scene. When newspaper reporters arrived there was the Dymaxion Car by itself, smashed and bloody. The news accounts, then, placed the blame for death and injury on the Dymaxion Car alone. TWO ZEP RIDERS KILLED AS FREAK CAR CRASHES, blazed one headline. THREE WHEELED CAR KILLS DRIVER, read another. Public opinion was molded by these stories.

A cable from England told Bucky that the group there was no longer interested in an automobile that had proven to be a death trap. In vain, Bucky and Captain Williams presented evidence to show that the Dymaxion Car had in no way been the cause of the accident. No one believed them or seemed to care.

To make matters worse, the Chrysler Corporation in 1934 unveiled a new model — the Airflow Chrysler. This streamlined car was nothing like the Dymaxion Car. As a matter of fact the Airflow car was popular only for a short time, then Chrysler returned to standard forms of the auto body. But again, the timing was just right to make all other auto manufacturers lose interest in the possibilities of the Dymaxion design.

Bucky did manage to turn out a second Dymaxion Car, and finally a third one. Both were sold. But no one in the industrial world seemed to care any more for Bucky's design for the future.

His money was gone. Once more, R. Buckminster Fuller, the successful failure, had to turn and face the reality of a world that was not ready to accept him or his ideas.

6

The Corncrib That
Became a House

In 1936, Bucky Fuller found himself without money and
without a job.

But the Great Depression had eased, though the crisis
was not completely passed. Slowly the federal government, under the leadership of President Franklin D.
Roosevelt, began to restore the sick economy of the country. Many different federal projects gave new hope to
men who thought they would never work again. The nation's factories were coming alive once more.

Now there was more protection for the American citi-
zen against the possible recurrence of such a national
calamity. A Social Security Act had been passed by the
Congress, giving pensions to all citizens past the age of
65. The federal government began to take a hand in con-
trolling the extremes to which businessmen could go in
making profits. A Securities and Exchange Commission
was created and given power to prevent wild speculation
in the stock market.

The Dymaxion Car, despite its lack of acceptance by
the motor industry, had made Bucky's name known to
manufacturers all over the country. So, after the third

Dymaxion Car was finished and sold, he had no trouble finding a job. He was hired by the Phelps Dodge Corporation, a large industrial group specializing in metal products. Bucky was asked to create a Department of Research and Development, where new ideas for inventions could be explored. American industry was just beginning to wake up to the fact that such a department would eventually become the brain center of an entire industrial complex. Before this, research was thought of as something that went on in college laboratories, not in manufacturing plants.

Anne Fuller was certainly pleased at the thought of a steady, weekly salary coming into the house. But she knew Bucky well enough to realize that money could only play a secondary role in their lives. The Phelps Dodge position was going to give Bucky a chance to use his imagination and his ideas — that was far more important to her than his paycheck. Still, with Allegra growing up, the money was going to be useful.

Bucky proved useful to the Phelps Dodge Corporation also. He invented a new kind of brake for automobiles, using a brake drum made of bronze instead of steel. One of the difficulties that had been plaguing the company was the intense heating up of steel brakes during the act of hard and rapid braking. This heating caused brakes to grab, or to slip. Bucky's bronze drums were arranged to carry heat away very rapidly. Thus the stopping time of a brake could be reduced tremendously without losing efficiency. Another Fuller invention was a method of processing a particular ore of the metal, tin, that had resisted all previous efforts to melt it down.

While he was doing this kind of inventing for Phelps Dodge, Bucky was doing other things at home. He began writing a series of essays in which he looked at the inefficiency with which the world was run. In the essays he proposed ways of using the available energy of the universe to provide all the necessities of life for every man, woman, and child on the earth. He wrote about his ideas for changing the housing industry into an efficient industrial machine that would turn out houses to sell as cheaply as cars. In angry, sarcastic language, he quarreled with the businessmen and bankers who were afraid to face up to the changes that scientific and technological progress had made necessary. These people, now in power, would have to realize that the real wealth of the world was *energy*, and not gold. The world was going to have to change its ways.

Bucky called his collection of essays *Nine Chains to the Moon*. He chose this title from the simple, statistical fact that if all the people in the world were to stand upon one another's shoulders, they would form a human chain 2,160,000 miles long, a chain that would go back and forth between earth and moon nine times. "If it is not so far to the moon, then it is not so far to the limits of the universe — whatever, whenever, or wherever they may be," Bucky wrote.

He was able to interest the New York publishing house of J. B. Lippincott in his manuscript. In 1938, *Nine Chains to the Moon* appeared in the bookstores. A review of the book in the popular magazine, *Newsweek*, declared: "Imagine a three-ring circus — high wire acts, blaring bands, clowning and all — with one man as the whole show . . . this book is at once a guide book and dream book of the future, a purge of the past, a debunker of architecture, economics, politics . . . this ruddy-faced, gray-haired inventor is no nut! It's great stuff!"

Other reviews were lukewarm. Most readers complained that Bucky used an outlandish kind of language to express his ideas. For example: "Thus genius has the ability to 'fix' events by the convergent angle of two or more sight 'lines,' not only in time (or space) past, but, also, in time (or space) ahead, from the central perspective of self-NOW." What in the name of all that was holy did that mean? What Bucky was saying in his explosive, dramatic way was that any genius can see relationships between things that are invisible to ordinary men.

Nine Chains to the Moon made only a ripple in the book market. But in it, bold and clear, was R. Buckminster Fuller's challenge to the world.

Meanwhile Bucky had been able to interest his superiors at the Phelps Dodge Corporation in one of his earlier creations — the Dymaxion Bathroom. This was the bathroom he had created for the 4-D house, the one-piece, efficient room that operated on only one quart of water.

Here at Phelps Dodge were great metal presses, easily capable of stamping out parts for the Dymaxion Bathroom. The research staff, under Bucky's direction, worked out new and more efficient ways of mass-producing these bathrooms, complete with ventilating, lighting, heating, and plumbing equipment. There were two major sections: the tub-shower component, and the lavatory-toilet component. The whole bathroom was stamped out of four pieces of steel which were then welded together to look like a single surface. There were no sharp corners, only smooth and graceful curves.

The entire bathroom covered an area five feet square! And every bit of space was used so efficiently that there was even room for a medicine cabinet large enough to hold a five-gallon bucket.

There seemed to be universal approval of the Dymaxion Bathroom. Even the plumbers appeared to like it. An article praising Bucky's invention appeared in the official magazine of the New York Plumbers Association, *The Ladle*. Preparations went ahead full steam for production of the units. Twelve complete bathrooms came off the assembly line. Bucky's novelist friend, Christopher Morley, bought two of them for his Long Island home. A man who had once been Secretary of the Navy, John Nicholas Brown, had two installed in his house.

And then production of the Dymaxion Bathroom was stopped.

When Bucky tried to find out what had happened, he was referred to a more important executive in the chain of command. Finally, he discovered that one of Phelps Dodge's best customers, Standard Sanitary-American Radiator Company, makers of bathtubs, sinks, and toilets, were very worried about unfavorable reactions of the plumbers' unions all over the country to the Dymaxion unit. The Phelps Dodge executives had not been willing to produce an item that might result in the refusal by plumbers to place any of their products in homes.

Bucky tried to point out that these fears were unfounded. Hadn't the plumbers themselves praised the Dymaxion Bathroom in their magazine? Didn't they realize that this kind of bathroom meant more work for plumbers, and not less? After all, bathrooms were permanent fixtures. Once a plumber had put in a bathroom, he was through with it — except for occasional repairs. But the Dymaxion Bathroom had been planned to go along with people who moved, like furniture. Plumbers would be called in to plumb the bathroom, just as electricians had to be called to wire appliances. And this would happen every time a family moved. But the minds of those who controlled production had been made up; Bucky's arguments went unheeded.

Again, the Fuller luck had run out. Another attempt to make man's living on earth simpler and more efficient had been frustrated. More in sadness than in anger, he left his position with Phelps Dodge in 1938 and sought work elsewhere. This time, he found a new kind of job.

In 1930, the successful publisher of a news magazine called *Time*, Henry R. Luce, had started another magazine which he called *Fortune*. Already a hit by 1938, *Fortune* was a rather expensive-looking magazine, with deluxe paper and illustrations, which devoted itself to news and problems in the world of business.

Bucky's new ideas and inventions were appealing to the editors of *Fortune*, and they offered him the position of science consultant and editor. Bucky accepted quite readily. Here was a chance not only to get his ideas into print, but also to have them read by virtually every important businessman and manufacturer in the world.

During the two years he worked for *Fortune*, Bucky

was able to accomplish what he considered to be a most
important task. No one had ever really added up all the
energy resources of the world. This information was
vital, if science and technology were to be used to their
best advantage for man's progress. He persuaded the editors that he was the man to do this job.

The first thing he did was to use all possible means —
libraries, universities, government offices — to gather information about all the countries in the world. He was
interested in items like the number of tons of coal or
barrels of petroleum used for industrial power every
year. He wanted to know how many kilowatt-hours of
electrical power were being used, and how many gallons
of water flowing per second were needed to generate that
power. He checked and double-checked the population
statistics of all the countries on every continent.

At that time the world population distributed itself
over the globe in this fashion: Asia had about 50%,
Europe about 24%, and Africa about 12%. The rest of
the population was divided between North America
(8%), South America (4%), Central America (1%),
and all other countries (1%).

Then Bucky devised a unit that he called the "energy
slave." The calculation of such a unit was rather complicated; but the energy slave unit showed most clearly the
difference between those parts of the world that were
technologically advanced and those that were not. In the
science of physics, mechanical energy can be defined in
terms of how much of it is needed to move a weight
against the force of gravity. For example, the energy

used to move a weight of one pound up through a distance of one foot is one *foot-pound*.

Bucky calculated that all the countries in the world were using something over 80 quintillion (80,000,000,000,000,000,000) foot-pounds. But only about 1/25th of this was being converted into useful work by man, making a total of about $3\frac{1}{5}$ quintillion foot-pounds of efficiently used energy. In one eight-hour day a single man was capable of doing about 15,000 foot-pounds of useful work. In a work year of 250 days, then, a man would accomplish 37,500,000 foot-pounds.

If you then divided the total amount of efficiently used energy in the world by the total work-year's energy used for work by one man, you arrived at a figure equal to about $85\frac{1}{2}$ billion (85,500,000,000) foot-pounds. This was the amount of energy Bucky thought of as being enslaved by man for useful work; this was one "energy slave."

When he had figured out the number of energy slaves per inhabitant for each country, Bucky was able to show a fantastic discrepancy between the continents of the world. Asia, the most populous, had only two energy slaves for each person who lived on that huge continent. And the continent of North America with only 8% of the total population had 347 energy slaves for each inhabitant! South America and Europe were about even; the first had 28 energy slaves, the second, 27. Africa had only 13 energy slaves per inhabitant. Now Bucky could demonstrate without any doubt that it was a lack of useful energy — energy that only technological progress could supply — that was keeping many nations from catching up with the twentieth century.

Another creation of Bucky's at this time was what he called his World Energy Map. He divided the surface of a sphere into squares and triangles in a very special way. If this were done to a globe of the earth, and then if the skin of the globe (that is, the map of the world) were removed and stretched flat, the earth became divided very neatly into continents that were linked together, with the oceans all around on the outside. Bucky's map showed the earth was made up of two distinctive parts, a land grouping and a water grouping.

Two years later, Bucky was asked to develop this kind of map even further for *Life*, the widely read picture magazine of the *Time-Fortune* group. He needed no urging. Within a few months he turned out a new version that he called the Dymaxion Map.

With the spherical surface of the earth sliced into various combinations of squares and triangles, Bucky's map could show all the geographical data of the world without any breaks in the contours of the continents. Moreover, unlike maps based on the most common method of projecting the spherical world on to a flat surface, the Dymaxion Map had no distortions.

In the Mercator method of projection, the skin of the globe is unrolled like a cylinder, so that all the lines of longitude become parallel north and south lines. Of course, these lines really all stretch between the North and South Poles. The result of such a projection is that the Arctic and Antarctic areas are distorted from their natural size. Thus, the Mercator projection map is fine for short-distance nagivation, but quite disastrous for global flying or course planning for intercontinental rockets.

Life published the Dymaxion Map in March of 1943. Once more, the name of R. Buckminster Fuller was signed to a notice to the world: be ready for change! Whether it was autos or maps, Bucky was determined to keep this message before the eyes of mankind.

Another great opportunity came for Bucky in 1940 — a chance to do something with the plans for the Dymaxion House. While driving with his friend Christopher Morley through the farmlands of Missouri, Bucky pointed out the cylindrical steel bins in which farmers kept their grain and corn.

There was an efficient kind of house for you! It could be manufactured on an assembly line as a prefabricated house; that is, the factory could turn out a few large parts that could easily be assembled to make a house. It would cost less than a dollar for each square foot of floor space to house a family in such a ready-made house! What was the secret?

There was no secret. It was simple high-school geometry. If you took a cube, where you have six square walls each the same size, and change it into a cylinder, the same wall area encloses more space. While Morley drove on, Bucky scribbled some diagrams and calculations on the back of an envelope:

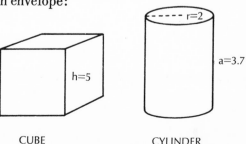

CUBE   CYLINDER

Suppose a cylinder has a base radius of 2 and a height of 5. The area of the surface of the cylinder involves the radius, the height, and the constant number, *pi*, which can be written as $22/7$ for simplicity. Then:

Area = $(2)(pi)r(r + h) = (88/7)(7) = 88$.

Now a cube with a side equal to some unknown number, *a*, has a surface area = $6a^2$. So, if we set the area value 88 equal to this and solve for *a*, we get a value of about 3.7. The volume of a cube is found this way:

Volume = $a^3 = (3.8)(3.8)(3.8) =$ about 55.

But the volume of a cylinder is found by:

Volume = $(pi)(r^2)(h) = (22/7)(4)(5) =$ about 63.

So, the cylinder contains much more useful space than the cube! Not only that, but the circular base of the cylinder takes up less ground space than the square base of the cube.

Having proved his point, Bucky went on to describe how he would build his cylindrical house. There would be no need for internal supports, nor for external bracing. Such houses would be easier to heat and to keep cool. Morley was impressed. Why didn't Bucky go ahead and build them?

Bucky had the answer to that on the tip of his tongue. Money. Money that would give him time to work out plans, that would take care of little, but important details, like travel and hotel expenses. Money always seemed to be a basic problem.

But Chris Morley was a true friend. He had just written a new novel called *Kitty Foyle*. Perhaps it would become popular and make money. And, if Bucky would permit the favor, he would donate the profits from the book toward the manufacture of Buck's cylinder houses.

Kitty Foyle was not only a best seller; it was also sold to a motion picture company. Morley was true to his word. Bucky could begin whenever he was ready.

It took many weeks to prepare careful plans for the cylindrical house, which Bucky named the Dymaxion Deployment Unit. Now the problem was: where could the house be manufactured? The answer came at once. Why not have the Dymaxion Unit made by the very people who manufactured the storage bins they had seen in the fields?

That company was the Butler Manufacturing Company of Kansas City. Since their machinery was all geared for the production of steel cylinders, very few changes would have to be made to produce Bucky's house. After a few weeks of conversation, the company officials were favorably impressed. They agreed to manufacture the Dymaxion Unit.

The major departure from the corncrib shape in Bucky's design was the roof. Atop the steel cylinders made by the Butler Company, the roof was a simple, sharp-pointed cone. Bucky curved the bottom rim of the cone into rounded eaves that fitted onto the top of the cylinder. His first intention had been to make the appearance of the house more graceful. However, he soon discovered that curving the eaves in this fashion added great strength to the entire structure.

The cylinder that formed the walls of the house had a diameter of twenty feet, which made for a floor area of a little over three hundred square feet. By this time many of the new materials envisaged by Bucky had been invented and were being sold on the market. One of these was a new kind of wool-like material actually made from fine filaments spun out of molten glass and called *fiber glass*. This protective layer between the outer steel wall and inner wallboard served to keep the heat inside in winter and outside in summer. Under the ceiling, he placed a three-inch thickness of fiber glass. This wonderful new stuff turned out to be excellent for absorbing sound, as well as for insulating.

How do you make windows in a cylindrical wall that curves at every point? Bucky solved this problem by calling upon his experience in the Navy. He had round portholes cut into the sides. More natural light was made available by adding a skylight and ventilator at the top of the roof cone. Rooms were fashioned out of the cylindrical space by sections of weighted curtains that could be easily pushed aside to merge rooms into a single space. This was an idea that Bucky had worked out for the original 4-D house.

Assembling the Dymaxion Deployment Unit was a simple task. First, the conical roof was assembled and hoisted into the air on a mast. Then, the cylindrical walls were assembled beneath the cone. This part of the assembly could be done by men standing comfortably on the ground. Finally, the roof was lowered slowly over the top of the cylinder, until the curved eaves made a tight fit.

One unusual incident made the engineers of the Butler Company keenly aware of Bucky's understanding of scientific principles. On a hot August day in 1940, a group of them came out to see the first Dymaxion Unit. The Unit was hoisted on its mast slightly above the prepared brick and earth floor on which it was to rest. When Bucky invited them to enter the house, the engineers balked. If it was over a hundred degrees outside, they said, surely the inside of that metal house baking in the sun would be like the interior of a blast furnace.

Bucky smiled. No, he disagreed, that wouldn't be the case. As a matter of fact, the inside of the house would be much cooler than the outside atmosphere. Did he notice a look of doubt on their faces? Well, then, why didn't they go in?

The engineers were unprepared for the shock. The house was as cool as though it were air-conditioned! But there was no air-conditioning machinery to be seen. Was it magic?

Bucky assured them that they were observing a basic behavior of gases known to any physicist. The engineers lighted cigarettes; the movement of the smoke would give them a clue to what the air inside the cylinder was doing. In a few moments, they had the answer: the air was rushing down from the top ventilator hole and going out through the space between the brick floor and the walls.

It all seemed unreal. Hot air was supposed to rise — everyone knew that. But here the air was doing exactly the opposite.

Bucky explained. The ocean of air around us can be full of currents, like the sea. And the temperature of these currents depends really upon the energy of the gases in the different spots. After all, the Gulf Stream in the Atlantic is a warm current flowing through a much colder ocean.

All around the walls of the Dymaxion House, the air was being heated by the sun. And this very hot air was indeed becoming lighter and was rising. How does this rising current keep supplied? Why, by pulling out more air from under the Dymaxion House. And this pulling out caused a downflow of air inside the house, a downflow containing a cold draft. The engineers were amazed. Here was a house being cooled without the use of fans.

Now Bucky was convinced that his venture would be successful. Interest in the Dymaxion Deployment Unit spread rapidly. And for the first time an interest in Bucky's work was shown by certain units of the American armed forces.

In 1939, the democratic nations of the world had begun to awaken to the fact that a major portion of the earth was being governed by men who were threatening to put an end to democracy everywhere. By 1940, Japan had established points of attack on the Chinese mainland. Not satisfied with conquering China alone, the Japanese leaders had ordered an advance into French Indochina. It looked as though the *samurai* were setting out to conquer the world.

When Hitler marched into Poland, England and France declared war against Germany. But these two democratic nations had not prepared for war as well as had their enemy. The army Britain sent into France was smashed and defeated by June of 1940. By a great miracle, the famous rescue of British and French soldiers from the beach at Dunkirk in northern France had saved over 300,000 fighting men. But on the twenty-second of June, France gave up. England faced the German conqueror of Europe alone.

In the United States, the people and the government watched events in Europe and Asia with mixed feelings. Some felt that America, with a large ocean on either side, was comparatively safe from invasion. Others insisted that England ought to be helped. Still others urged the government to aid the persecuted Jews of Europe. There were also many who felt that Hitler was a fine leader who had prevented Germany from becoming a Communist country. The ability of the Nazis to move swiftly and seize power was admired by many Americans. Some pointed out that sooner or later Hitler and Stalin would destroy one another, and that Americans would be better off for not interfering in Europe's affairs.

In the autumn of 1940, Hitler launched an all-out attack on British cities from the air. Hundreds of German bombers filled the skies over England in an effort to wipe out the Royal Air Force. But thanks to a new electronic invention called *radar*, the British were able to anticipate these raids and shoot down many bombers. Then followed awful nights of bombing over all large cities in England. It was clear that Hitler was determined to terrorize the English into submitting. But the English people held fast, and Hitler did not succeed.

Now the armed forces of the United States began to be interested in the new inventions being used by the British. When Hitler made the decision to invade the Soviet Union in June of 1941, the American government began to see that it would be necessary to come to the assistance

of both England and Russia. Yet Germany seemed reluctant to declare war on the United States, even when sup-
plies began to flow to her enemies from America.

This was when the Army Signal Corps representatives
came to see Buckminster Fuller's Dymaxion Deployment
Unit at the Butler Company in Kansas City, Missouri.
The Signal Corps was badly in need of some kind of
light, easily transported, easily assembled hut in which
radar equipment could be set up and operated. The military men were impressed by the efficiency and low cost of
the Dymaxion Unit. Bucky had figured the cost of one
Unit, fully furnished and with attached cylindrical bathroom, at only $1,250. And this price included an icebox
and stove that were both operated by kerosene.

Bucky explained to the Army visitors how his
Dymaxion Unit fulfilled the idea of doing more with
less. He showed them how he had employed new materials in new ways. For example, the porthole windows
were not made of glass. For these he had used a new
transparent acrylic plastic which had previously been
used only for the canopies of war planes. The floor onto
which the Unit was lowered was made of flat steel sheets
which served as a moisture barrier. Over these were
placed rectangles of a hard, pressed wood material called
masonite. Nothing was glued or nailed together. But
Bucky had found out that masonite tended to curl in such
a way that one side — the shiny side — was arched outward. He had laid the sheets shiny side up, so that the
pull of gravity kept the whole floor perfectly flat.

Architects, too, heard about Bucky's strange new
house, and came to see and test it. One of the Units was

installed in a Washington, D.C., park for study by officials of a government housing agency. Another became a special garden exhibit in the garden of the Museum of Modern Art in New York City.

Orders for hundreds, and soon some thousands, of Dymaxion Deployment Units came from both the Army Signal Corps and Army Air Corps. One major area in which these houses were most useful was on the coast of the Persian Gulf. This was a transfer point where American fighter planes were delivered to Russian pilots. The Dymaxion Units served as dormitories for American pilots and mechanics. In a few months, Bucky's live-in cylinders were being erected in different parts of the earth, as the United States Army began to place radar stations in strategic places.

On the morning of December 7, 1941, the Japanese warlords made their bid for supremacy of the Pacific Ocean by bombing the American Fleet at Pearl Harbor. Now, the United States could no longer be "officially" neutral. She joined Britain and the Soviet Union as partners in war against the Axis, the name given to those countries that had united to bring death and destruction to the world.

It seemed strange that during the previous ten years when the United States had been at peace, few people had paid attention to Bucky's plans for solving the shelter problems of man. Now the rage and destruction of the Second World War, the struggle between the powers that wanted to enslave man and those that wanted to keep him free, had changed everything. His Dymaxion House was not just a dream of the improbable future — it was a real invention that had proved its usefulness. The name of R. Buckminster Fuller was being mentioned in high government circles. He was no longer being written off as an eccentric inventor who talked endlessly about things no one understood.

It was 1942. America was in the throes of trying to stop the Japanese from taking over the Pacific Islands. The need for thousands of guns and millions of bullets and shells was making steel a very scarce item. The Butler Manufacturing Company could not get enough steel to keep making the Dymaxion Units. Soon they had to be scratched from the production list.

But the stopping of production did not spell failure for Bucky. The war had changed his life in other ways. He decided to give up his bad habits of drinking and smoking; in fact, he cut these out completely from his life. He realized, he told Anne, that a man could not drink and be a prophet of the future at the same time. People tended to dismiss his talk as the babbling of a drunkard. Now that the acceptance of the Dymaxion Unit had given him a start, Bucky was determined to keep moving forward.

His first action in this direction was to accept the job that had been offered to him in Washington, D.C. He became Director of the Mechanical Engineering Section of a new, important government agency — the Board of Economic Warfare.

He was now forty-seven years old.

7

The House That Failed

HITLER and the other members of the Axis expected to win the war they had begun. But they had sadly underestimated the fantastic ability of American industry to meet the needs of an emergency situation. By 1944, factories in the United States were pouring out thousands of fighter planes, bombers, warships, merchant ships, guns, shells, bullets, and uniforms. Millions of men who had never had an inkling of what it was like to be a soldier or to be in a war had been whipped into strong and spirited groups of fighting men, ready to defend their way of life against an invasion by the few who wished to dominate the earth.

The removal of so many men from industry meant that there were more jobs than people. Women were recruited to do work in shipyards and factories that had never been done by women before. One of the songs sung and whistled by everyone was "Rosie, the Riveter." In many cities, factories were running on a twenty-four-hour basis, three shifts a day. Rooms were hard to find; often, the same bed was being shared by three different people, one coming in to sleep just as another awakened for work.

This was the situation in the city of Wichita, Kansas, in 1944. But suddenly workers in the Beech Aircraft Company in that city began quitting their jobs to find work in other cities. No one knew exactly why this was happening, but some labor union leaders felt that the workers expected many fewer airplanes would be built when the war was over, and then they would be out of jobs. At that time, no one seemed to see the possibilities of commercial aviation.

What the aircraft industry needed was some kind of proof that it could go on employing a large number of people after the war. The problem of finding this proof was referred to the Labor Department in Washington. There, someone remembered a man named R. Buckminster Fuller who had said something about being able to turn out houses in the same assembly line way as airplanes. Where was Fuller? Why, he was right there in Washington, immediately available for advice.

Bucky had the answer to the problem right away. The aircraft industry had made tremendous progress during the war. In fact, many of the new alloys and other products that had not been available during the late 20's, when the 4-D House had been created, were now being used. To change from making aluminum alloy parts for airplanes to aluminum alloy parts for houses was a simple matter. The industry could certainly switch to manufacturing Dymaxion Houses in a very short time. Actually, Bucky pointed out, two problems could be solved at once. The industry would be saved, and adequate, cheap housing could be provided at once to ease the housing shortage, not only in the United States, but in countries all over the world.

Under the prodding of officials of the International Order of Machinists, the Beech Aircraft Company of Wichita agreed to finance the planning and setting up of an experimental assembly line for the manufacture of the Dymaxion House. Bucky resigned from his Washington position and went to Kansas. His greatest opportunity for success seemed to have arrived.

While the first parts were being turned out, Bucky was asked to speak to the aircraft workers about the Dymaxion House. His typically exciting way of describing his own ideas was infectious. Soon fewer and fewer workers were leaving Wichita. Impressed by Bucky's ability to halt the drain of people from the aircraft industry, the Army Air Force ordered the first two Dymaxion Houses for use in the Pacific Theater of the war.

Bucky had changed a few of the original aspects of the Dymaxion House. Instead of little porthole windows, a full strip of Plexiglas went around the entire circumference of the wall. The house dome stood sixteen feet high, covering about 12,000 cubic feet of space. But the parts for a single house could be packed and shipped in only 300 cubic feet! Bucky estimated that counting all costs, the Dymaxion House, completely installed, would cost only about $6,500 — the price of an expensive automobile.

Enthusiasm for the Wichita Dymaxion House in-

creased. It seemed evident that the average American
housewife looked upon Bucky's house as her idea of a
dream house — spacious, yet easy to clean, efficient, yet
charming. *Fortune,* the magazine that had been Bucky's
past employer, noted that the Wichita House was so radi-
cally different, that it could not be compared honestly
with existing houses.

Meanwhile, the Allies persisted in their efforts against
the Axis powers. In June, 1944, the invasion of Hitler's
Europe began. At the same time, American troops were
beginning to recapture strategic Pacific Islands, one at a
time, from the Japanese. By May of 1945, Germany's
great army had been ground to bits; conquerors no more,
the German generals surrendered.

Japan's final defeat occurred, not by the invasion of
Japan itself, but by the by-product of a scientific discovery made in 1939. In that year, two German scientists,
Lisa Meitner and Otto Frisch, showed that the uranium
atom could be split by an atomic bullet, the neutron, with
the resulting release of a tremendous amount of energy.
Albert Einstein, the great theoretical physicist who had
left Germany to live in the United States, wrote a letter to
President Roosevelt in 1942, suggesting that this kind of
atomic energy could be used as a military weapon, and
that it might be a good idea for America to develop this
weapon before the Germans did. The result, of course,
was the first atomic bomb — the A-bomb — that was
dropped on Hiroshima, Japan, on August 6, 1945. Three
days later, a second A-bomb fell on the city of Nagasaki.
More than 100,000 people were killed by the two bombs.

In the face of this new horror, Japan could not go on. On September 2, 1945, the formal surrender of the Japanese took place.

World War II was over.

Within a few months, members of America's great civilian army were returning to their homes and families. They wore on their uniforms the little gold button, known familiarly as "the Ruptured Duck," that was the symbol of an honorable discharge for a job well done. Suddenly, the labor shortage ended. There was still a housing shortage; but it seemed to have nothing to do with industry or labor.

Bucky's Wichita House had just reached the point where full production could be planned and begun. This meant that the tools for the major assembly line sections had to be acquired and set up. The price for this readying was about ten million dollars. Bucky waited for the Beech Aircraft Company executives to give the word to go ahead, but with the war ending, and with thousands of trained pilots returning to civilian life, the Beech Company saw a sure success in the increase of a demand for small private planes. They decided to put all their finances and industrial effort into producing these, and not houses. After all, they had not actually given Bucky written guarantees that they would produce his house.

Of course, Buckminster Fuller understood their problems perfectly. But now, at the age of fifty, he had to turn to other fields of activity and interest.

8

Nature's Own Geometry

EVER SINCE his elementary school years at Milton Academy, Bucky Fuller had thought about geometry. He remembered how difficult it had been for him to accept the kind of geometry he had been taught. What nonsense it was for a teacher to talk about nonexistent points, lines, and planes as though they were real!

Was this geometry made up by man actually the geometry of nature herself? Or did nature have a special kind of geometry, a collection of basic forms, upon which man had yet to stumble?

All through the years that followed his graduation from the "ninety-day wonder" ensign class at the Naval Academy in 1917, Bucky had managed to spend some time thinking about the geometry of nature. Over and over again, he asked himself why man's geometry seemed to come out with such strange, never-ending constant numbers like *pi*. Chemists carried on their science on the assumption that chemical elements always combined in terms of simple whole numbers. Could it be that the geometry of nature was basically as simple as the combining of atoms?

Inevitably, he turned to the subject that was always uppermost in his mind — energy.

From his observations, Bucky began to build in his mind a kind of model of how energy existed in different structures. It seemed to him that one could suppose that there were two kinds of energies: first, the energies that were related to forces that compressed, or pushed together; second, those energies related to forces that pulled apart. In nature, there seemed to be a tendency for these two kinds of energy to be balanced; that is, nature tended to keep these energies in a state of *equilibrium.*

Suppose a bridge had to be built across a river. The main problem was to achieve this kind of equilibrium in the bridge structure. But the bridge was made of metals, and the metals were made of chemical atoms. You could say that the tiny atoms were in themselves energetic structures in a state of equilibrium.

Was there some basic geometric form in nature that represented this energy equilibrium? Would it be the same form for large structures as for atoms?

Bucky began to play a strange game during the evenings. He used a number of small spheres, all the same size. The game was to see how the spheres could be stacked together as closely as possible about a central sphere. First, he would put down one sphere:

Then around it could go six more, each touching the first:

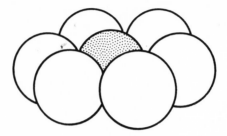

But only three more on each side could be added to touch the center sphere:

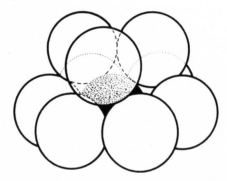

The outside layer, then, was always composed of twelve spheres.

Bucky felt that somehow he had stumbled across a law of nature. This pattern of crowding together was one that always occurred in the universe, where all matter was built out of atoms that were crowded together in the same way. He experimented further and discovered that a second layer of spheres, put down to cover the first completely, always had exactly forty-two spheres. The third layer took ninety-two to complete.

What name could he give to this pattern of spheres? Bucky decided that the most obvious name would be "the closest packing of spheres." He did not know that many years before, about the time he was born, a scientist named Barlow had already suggested this principle as one way of describing how atoms were structured in common salt, and in other crystalline forms of matter. Nor did Bucky know that at about the same time he was beginning his sphere-packing game an English physicist named Sir William Bragg had shot x-rays through crystals in an effort to uncover crystalline structure. Bragg had found the same kind of patterns as had Bucky. Of course, the English scientist knew nothing of a wild-eyed American inventor named R. Buckminster Fuller. But Bragg chose Barlow's description of *closest-packing* for the atomic arrangements he found in crystals.

Playing his game further, Bucky discovered that he could predict the number of spheres in a closest-packing model by using a simple mathematical formula:

$$10 \times (\text{the number of layers})^2 + 2 = \text{the total number of spheres.}$$

Thus, for the first layer:

$$10 \times (1)^2 + 2 = 12,$$

for the second:

$$10 \times (2)^2 + 2 = 42,$$

and so on.

This seemed like a beautiful kind of natural number magic to Bucky. He kept looking for ways in which he could link this idea of closest packing to nature itself.

He tried imagining geometrical plane surfaces that would be just touching, or tangent to the spherical outer layers:

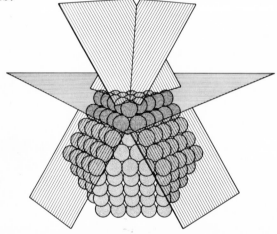

To his surprise, the planes did not form what he had expected — a regular solid figure. Instead, the planes met to form a fourteen-sided polyhedron, made up of eight triangles and six squares.

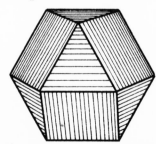

Bucky sat up for many nights, trying to puzzle out the meaning of such a strange polyhedron.

One night he found his first clue.

The sides of each of the fourteen faces were all the same length, whether they bounded triangle or square. The lines met in twelve points, or *vertices*, of the polyhedron. And the lines from each of the vertices to the inner center of the figure were all equal to the lines that formed the external faces! What did that mean?

Bucky began to think about his fourteen-sided figure in terms of forces — pushes and pulls, stresses and strains. He knew that in physics, a force was defined as a measurable quantity. In fact, in order to measure a force completely, you had to know *two* things about it: how strong it was, and in which direction the force was pointed. Such a two-measurement quantity was called a *vector*.

It seemed to Bucky that he could think about this geometrical figure in two ways. First, it was being "held in" by all the equal *outside* lines that joined the vertices:

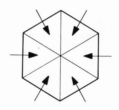

Then, it was also being "pushed out" by all the equal lines that radiated from the inner center to the vertices:

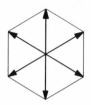

Since all these "holding in" and "pushing out" lines were exactly the same length, you could say that this figure represented a kind of stalemate of forces, or an *equilibrium*. Yes, that was it. His closest-packing polyhedron really represented a *vector equilibrium* in nature.

But there was still more to uncover.

What would happen to the closest-packed spheres if you took out the center sphere? Bucky tried it.

The vector equilibrium changed. As the spheres readjusted their position to the creation of a center vacancy, more polyhedral planes could be formed. Six more sides were added; what was more strange, each of the sides was now an equilateral triangle. The vector equilibrium had become an *icosahedron* — the twenty-sided figure that was one of the five known regular polyhedrons.

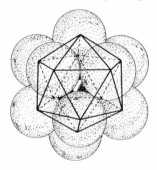

Now, suppose the icosahedron could be changed by taking some more spheres from the center. The radial forces pushing out would be weakened. What would happen?

To Bucky's surprise, the icosahedron shrank. It became another regular solid figure — the octahedron. This was made of two pyramids with their bases joined:

But there was yet another change that could take place. By more radial weakening, the octahedron collapsed into the simplest of the regular solid polyhedrons — the four-sided *tetrahedron*.

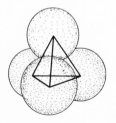

Here was rock bottom. Bucky felt, he *knew,* that he had arrived at the most fundamental geometric form in nature.

It took a long time for him to work out his system of nature's geometry. There were all the interruptions of living — taking care of Anne and Allegra, designing his Dymaxion House and Automobile, surviving all the failures, working for *Fortune* and Phelps Dodge and the federal government. There was the awful world war and the disappointment of the Wichita House.

But during his spare moments, during many of the hours on Bear Island when he could relax and just think, Bucky worked out the details of what he considered to be the real geometry of the universe.

As he read up on physics and chemistry, he found echoes of his geometry in those sciences. In his formula for predicting the total number of spheres the number of layers appeared as a *square* — the number times itself. Was this squared number related to other important squared numbers in physics? Newton's law of gravity related the force of gravity to the square of a radial distance.

$$F = \frac{G\, m_1 m_2}{R^2}$$

And Einstein's great discovery of the equality between mass and energy also had a squared number in it — the square of the speed of light:

$$E = mc^2$$

Measuring speed implied measuring distance; so, that formula, too, was concerned with the square of a radial measurement. More important, scientists were now getting a deeper insight into the way atoms combined to form molecules of matter. It looked as though the basic geometric formations of such molecules were the tetrahedron, the octahedron, and the icosahedron!

Encouraged, Bucky began to write down the basic rules of his geometry.

"The tetrahedron is a basic structural system, and all structure in the universe is made up of tetrahedronal parts."

What did he mean by the word *system?* Well, that was easy. Since Bucky wanted to have a practical geometry, not an idealized, abstract one like the geometry he had been taught in school, he decided to assume that a system was simply a *closed* pattern of vectors. The system always had an *inside* and an *outside,* or an internal and external part. In Bucky's geometry there was no such thing as an imaginary, infinite plane that extended on and on forever in all directions. If you chose any corner, or vertex, of a system, the angles around it had to be concave or convex, depending upon whether you were inside or outside the system.

In Bucky's geometry, the triangle is the figure that supports itself most rigidly with the least amount of effort. Therefore, whatever system you have, the pushes and pulls — we can call them the "energies" — will always move along triangle lines. If you have a cubic system, for example, the energy will move along the *diagonals* of the cube.

When Bucky made little models of his solid figures from nonrigid plastic straws, he found that his prediction was correct. The tetrahedron, the octahedron, and the icosahedron were the only three absolutely stable figures.

His next investigation was to find out what happened if you pushed the sides of these three basic polyhedrons outward. By making more and more triangles out of each side, Bucky found that each of them finally approached the perfect solid figure called a *sphere*.

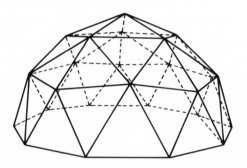

The vertices of the tetrahedron became points on the surface of the sphere. Through these vertices he could draw great circles on the surface. A *great circle* was one whose radius was the radius of the sphere itself. For example, you could consider the equator to be a great circle on the surface of the spherical earth.

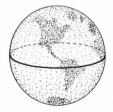 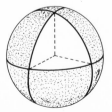

Now Bucky began to translate this change from polyhedron to sphere into the way forces would act in such a
system. He saw that the great circle bands between vertices represented the largest amount of pushing out by
the internal vectors of the system:

But if you drew the straight-line *chords* between these
vertices, you were then representing the largest amount
of pushing in by the external vectors of the system:

If the *external* vectors were greater, your sphere got
pushed back into the shape of a tetrahedron. Then, you
wound up with the solid figure that had the least amount
of space, or volume, and the greatest amount of surface.

If the *internal* vectors were greater, your tetrahedron
was blown out into spherical shape. Then, you had the
solid figure with the greatest amount of space, or volume,
and with the least amount of surface.

Bucky concluded that systems that were built up out
of combinations of symmetrical triangles provided the
best conditions for distributing energy. You could make
these triangles out of great circle chords joining vertices
on the surface of a sphere. By subdividing such triangles

into smaller and smaller ones, you could reach the point where your system provided the *greatest possible resistance* to inside or outside forces.

Bucky named the structure built up by this process a *geodesic* structure. The word *geodesic* actually meant "having to do with measuring the earth." But mathematicians had attached a different meaning to it; for them, any part of a great circle was a geodesic. So, in terms of the geometry of a sphere's surface, a geodesic was simply the shortest distance between two points on the surface. Albert Einstein had given a different meaning to the word. In his theory of relativity, he had called the paths of the planets about the sun geodesics; in general, the shortest curved path between two points taken by any body moving under the influence of a gravitational force could be considered a geodesic.

But what Bucky found most striking about his vector geometry was that irrational numbers like *pi* did not appear in it. He could combine up to twenty tetrahedrons to make up the other regular polyhedrons. Three tetrahedrons made up a cube. Four made up an octahedron. And twenty tetrahedrons made up the Vector Equilibrium! In fact, any and all polyhedron volumes could be calculated in combinations of tetrahedrons. So, such volumes were always a whole number times one tetrahedron. There was no need for a strange constant like 3.14159. . . .

You could really consider the tetrahedron a kind of "smallest possible lump" of space. All other spaces could be considered whole number multiples of this basic "lump." Physicists had already discovered that in nature all energy came in such "smallest possible lumps"; these energy "lumps" were called *quanta* (from the Latin word *quantum,* meaning a *bundle*). Bucky decided that the tetrahedron could be considered a *space* quantum that was equivalent to an energy quantum.

The year was 1947. Bucky felt that he was on the verge of making some kind of tremendous discovery. There was one gnawing question in his mind. Had he come upon a way to account for all the energy patterns of the universe?

9

Geodesic Domes for the World

WITH THE STOPPING of production of the Wichita House, Bucky Fuller had vowed never again to put his plans entirely in the hands of industrial corporations. Instead, he arranged his affairs so that industry would have to come to him.

In 1946, he organized and incorporated the Fuller Research Foundation. This gave him a legal means of protecting his ideas and inventions. All his research could be done in the name of the Foundation, and all copyrights and patents could be protected by it. Now he was ready to apply the principles of his synergetic-energetic geometry to the real world.

What excited him most were the possibilities of the geodesic. If you could construct a sphere made of the triangles formed by intersecting geodesics, each triangle would represent a tetrahedral structure of minimum surface and maximum strength. What if you sliced such a sphere in half? Then you would have a kind of covering, a covering in the shape of a dome, that would behave in an extraordinary way.

The architectural structure called the dome had fasci-

nated Bucky for many years. There were domes everywhere in nature — in caves, in bubbles, even in the fac-
eted eyes of insects. Eskimos lived in dome houses
shaped from snow blocks. In the Middle Ages, Euro-
peans had worshipped God in a dome house called a ca-
thedral. One of the most important dome structures in
architecture through the ages was the stone arch, where
one stone — the keystone — served to distribute the
weight of the arch stones properly.

One could make a play on words with *dome*. Look at
how many different ways there were of taking the two
letters *om* and adding front and back letters. *Dom* meant
house in many languages. Replace the *d* with an *h* and
add an *e* — there was *home*. When you died, you were
placed in the *tomb*. And when you were born, you
came out of the *womb*. Bucky felt that the idea of a
dome was an important one in the entire lifespan of
mankind.

Now, suppose you created a dome whose surface was a
number of joined-together tetrahedrons. It would be easy
enough to interlock the tetrahedron sides about geodesic
points as vertices. Then, you would have a multiple tetrahedral structure of least volume. But least volume was
the same as saying *least weight*. And along with least
weight, the structure would have maximum strength. Any
great load you would place on this dome would be spread
evenly out over the surface. The kind of material out of
which you built such a structure was, in a sense, unim-
portant. The dome could be made of paper; yet it should
not collapse under a heavy accumulation of snow, nor
should it blow down in a heavy gale.

It seemed to Bucky that he had finally realized one of his earliest goals: *to do the most with the least.* That was the message that was loud and clear in nature's own geometry.

From this Dymaxion geometry (Bucky stamped it with his own trademark), he arrived at another prediction about the behavior of a system. This prediction was related to his early vision of the dirigible house, where the different decks were supported by compression and tension forces. Why couldn't tetrahedrons be supported, one against the other, in the same way?

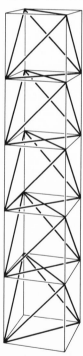

Slowly, the geometrical rules for such a compression-tension combination began to be worked out in his mind. You started with cubes, whose diagonals formed tetrahedrons that were pointing in the same direction.

The "weight" of each tetrahedron would be balanced exactly at the point called the center of gravity. For each tetrahedron you could imagine two radii going from the center of gravity to two of the vertices. You could also imagine that at each center of gravity, the radii were connected by a kind of ball bearing, so that they were free to swing together or pull apart.

Now Bucky could imagine one tetrahedron moving toward another one below it, with the centers of gravity connected by a "tension line." This line tended to pull center A toward center B and to pull center B toward A at the same time.

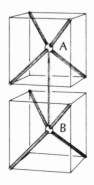

The radial lines from center A to vertices 3 and 4 in the upper tetrahedron then became like two legs that were being forced apart by the tension. The same thing was happening to the two radial lines that connected center B to vertices 1 and 2 of the lower tetrahedron. But these four radial lines could be kept from flying apart by connecting all the vertices to the centers and to each other.

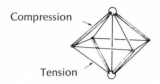

Bucky imagined an entire stack of such tensed and compressed tetrahedral radii, held together and, at the same time, kept at a minimal distance from one another.

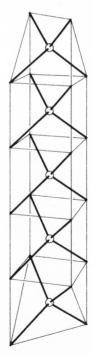

Could such a geometric structure be translated into real materials? He tried it with sticks (the radii from the centers of gravity) and string (the tension-compression lines).

It worked! The system could be arranged in a straight-line pattern, like a mast, or in a spherical dome shape. It was almost like magic. The wooden struts hung suspended in midair, kept in place by the balancing, unseen forces.

Bucky called this part of his geometry, *tensegrity*.

A third practical result of his geometry was the invention of the *octet truss*. This structure was Bucky's answer to the problem faced by architects and engineers when they had to use beams or struts of various kinds to support loads. Normally, such struts were laid parallel to one another on supporting walls:

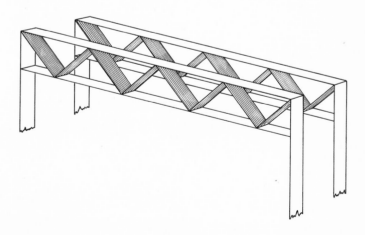

Thus, the ordinary truss, or framework to support some kind of load (as a roof), consisted of struts that supported independently of one another. One strut got no help from the next.

Bucky's truss consisted of tetrahedron or octahedron patterns combined into struts in such a way that they "curved back" into the whole system. Every strut "helped" the adjoining struts around it. The result was that any load on the octet truss was distributed evenly in all possible directions over the combined struts.

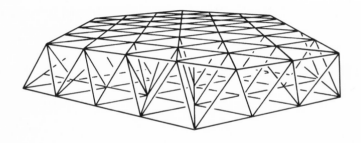

Bucky now turned away from industry and looked to the academic world for help. Beginning in 1948, he visited many colleges and universities, trying to interest professors and students in his new kind of geometry and construction. Not many professors would listen to him. The architects, as usual, considered him an outsider and not a professional. When he tried to explain the unusual results of his Dymaxion geometry to mathematicians, they smiled and said, yes, well, that was very interesting, but. When he tried to show physicists how his notion of internal and external energies were based upon clues that could be found in nature herself, they smiled and said, yes, well, that was rather clever for a nonphysicist, and wasn't he using words a bit too loosely.

But the artists and designers at many of these colleges were fascinated by what they heard. They listened to Bucky. And some of the younger architects and scientists began feeling a kinship with this short, heavy man who had the face and smile of a Dutch uncle, and who never seemed to tire of talking about the marvels that science and technology had in store.

Bucky managed to get himself invited to stay for a while at some of the colleges. At Chicago, he showed students of the Chicago Institute of Design how to make geodesic domes out of wooden sticks. He taught them to make prefabricated parts, triangles, pentagons, and hexagons, and to put these parts together to make domes.

In 1949, he was a guest of honor at Black Mountain College in North Carolina. This was a school where students performed manual labor while they learned. Later, he visited North Carolina State College at Raleigh. At both of these schools, eager young undergraduates worked with Bucky on model tetrahedron domes and tensegrity structures. There were many amazing variations that could be worked out for domes. Bucky made one that could be folded, like a butterfly's wings, into a light, flat package. When the package was opened and its circular base pulled taut, up popped a dome of great strength. Only about seven feet in diameter and made of flexible cable joined at the vertices, Bucky's dome could support the weight of more than eight people clinging to the top and sides.

No matter where Bucky went, it was the young people who clustered about to hear him talk about domes and the future of man's shelter problems. These students never seemed to tire of listening to him; and Bucky never seemed to grow weary of talking with them.

While Bucky was moving among colleges, his lawyer was preparing the patent applications for his new invention, the geodesic dome. Under the heading of Building Construction, the application began with these words:

"My invention relates to a framework for enclosing space."

Who would have thought that such a thing was patentable? A way of enclosing space! How could it be done? After all, almost any hollow body was a space encloser!

But Bucky knew that his way of enclosing space was different from any other way than had even been invented by man. He had seen the space of the universe from a different point of view. And that point of view was patentable! The patent laws of the United States would give him the right to keep others from using his techniques without permission.

Little by little, Bucky's traveling and demonstrating began to have an effect. Fuller's domes began to be talked about wherever architects gathered to discuss ideas. Some in the profession were suspicious; most merely unbelieving. Yet, in all this talk that went on there was this common thread: a fellow named Buckminster Fuller had gotten hold of something new, something that might turn out to be important.

A few young and talented "believers" came to stay with Bucky and to work with him on geodesic designs. Of course, he had no money to give them for their time and work. These devoted young people all faced the same decision this time that Bucky had had to face long before. What was more important to the person who felt he had something to offer to mankind, making a living or dedication to one's ideals? Bucky told them of his decision during that fateful year of 1927; a dedication to one's own felt genius came before all else. Somehow, you survived. And look, he, Bucky Fuller, had survived to fulfill his destiny. Some young people believed him and stayed on. Others felt that supporting a wife and children was their first obligation; unwillingly, these young men left Bucky to take secure jobs.

In 1952 came the first incredible stroke of luck. The Ford Motor Company was planning a new building at the River Rouge plant in Dearborn, Michigan. This building was to be an office building and showplace; it had been designed as a very modern "rotunda" — a cylindrical structure with fluted sides. Part of the design was a translucent dome that was to fit like a skylight over the top of the rotunda. There were not enough supports to carry the weight of a steel skylight framework. Somehow, word of Bucky's experiments came to the ears of Ford officials. They sent him their problem to solve.

Bucky's solution was an octet truss dome with a translucent plastic skin. He pointed out that whereas a conventional steel dome of the required ninety-three-foot diameter would weigh one hundred and sixty tons — far more than the building could support — his geodesic dome made of aluminium would weigh only eight and a half tons. Bucky's design captured the imagination of

Henry Ford II. The octet truss was just what he was looking for.

Since Bucky's application for a patent was already
filed, the Ford Motor Company could not build the dome
without permission. This meant that they had to pay
Bucky whatever he asked as a royalty, or licensing fee.
They received the first license to make a geodesic dome.
And it was the first time that Bucky could really control
the use of his ideas.

Once the dome had been planned, Bucky oversaw its
installation. This took only four months, a record for
that kind of construction. Finished in 1953, the Ford Rotunda Dome was an instant success with the American
public. People drove from everywhere in the United
States to see the building with Bucky's dome. It was the
first time a large number of people were able to visit and
see a large geodesic dome "in action." The effect of the
sunlight coming through the curved honeycomb of small
and large triangles was startling to the eye. Bucky began
to receive questions from people everywhere, asking
about his geodesic dome. Architects were clearly affected
by the success of the Rotunda Dome. The May 1953 issue
of the professional magazine, *Architectural Forum*, carried an article entitled, "Bucky Fuller Finds a Client;
Young Henry Ford Translates the Geodesic Dome into
Aluminum and Plastic."

Bucky's next action was to form two corporations:
Synergetics, Inc., and Geodesics, Inc., both in Raleigh,
near the college that had shown so much interest in him.
He hired some of his younger disciples as managers, designers, and planners. Anyone in the United States who

wished to build any kind of geodesic structure would
have to apply to these two companies for licensing and
consulting. And Bucky had a feeling that plenty of business would soon be coming his way.

By the early fifties, the United States and the Soviet
Union had settled into the political impasse known as the
"cold war." After the Second World War, Russia had
seized as much of the territory of Western Europe as she
could get, including Poland, Czechoslovakia, Hungary,
and a large chunk of Germany.

To counter this threat, the United States had built up a
military alliance with England, France, West Germany,
Turkey, and Greece known as NATO (North Atlantic
Treaty Organization). It began to appear as though the
civilized world was divided into two camps — the "free"
nations led by the United States, and the Communist dic-
tatorships led by the Soviet Union. These two powers
controlled whatever atomic weapons existed at the time,
and each knew that actual warfare might now mean the
end of man on earth. Yet, the stresses and strains of two
opposite philosophies of governing and living were almost like a real war.

In order to cope with the possibility of sudden atomic
attack by bomber or rocket missile, the Defense Department in Washington decided to set up a radar warning
line along the Arctic Circle in Alaska and Canada. The
code word for this project was DEW (Distant Early
Warning). But there were some serious problems to be
overcome. The weather was the enemy — harsh, freezing
cold that persisted for most of the year, and gales that
generated 200-mile-per-hour winds. Also, houses built to

withstand the weather had to be made of materials
through which shortwave radar signals could pass. This
meant that there could be no metal in their construction.

The problem was referred to Bucky. He worked out a
plastic radar dome (later shortened to "radome") that
was fifty-five feet in diameter and stood forty feet high.
These could be delivered by plane in knocked-down form
and assembled in only fourteen hours, six hours less than
the maximum time established by the Defense Department. A wind that blew at over 220 miles an hour could
not budge Bucky's plastic radome.

Another customer, the Marine Corps, became interested in the radome, and they sent people down to ask
Bucky questions. Could such domes be used as temporary shelters? If so, how easily could they be transported
from one place to another?

Bucky's answer was to design a geodesic dome made
of wooden frame and plastic skin with a thirty-foot diameter. Then he suggested to the Marines that the dome
could simply be picked up by helicopter and hauled
anywhere. This was an unusual idea, but it appealed to
the Marine agents. For Bucky, of course, it was an old
idea that had finally been translated into action. A form
of the movable dirigible house had finally arrived — a
dome home that could be moved from place to place by
aircraft. With the invention of the helicopter, this idea
had become a practical one.

The first airlift of a Fuller dome by helicopter took
place in February, 1954. The dome was picked up and,
as Bucky had predicted, flown without damage to another

spot. The streamlined shape of the dome minimized the drag of the air; the pilot did not feel his ship pulled to one side or the other. Cruising at a speed of about sixty miles an hour, the pilot returned the dome to its original resting place.

Now the Marines were really interested. How long would it take a group of Marines to erect such a dome from scratch on a beachhead? Why not let them do it and see, suggested Bucky. It took them about two hours and a quarter. Why waste all that time, they asked, couldn't the dome be erected on the deck of a carrier and flown completed to the beach? Good idea, said Bucky, let's try it. In fact, let's make a dome large enough to be a hangar for an aircraft and fly that to the beach.

It was done during a simulated attack on a beachhead and worked perfectly. As a result, the Marine Corps purchased more than three hundred of Bucky's domes and used them in many different parts of the world, even as far away as Antarctica.

In Italy, that year, the Tenth International Design Exhibition, known as the Triennale, was to be held. Architects and industrial designers from all over the world competed for prizes at this exhibition. But in 1954 the United States did not have an entry.

Bucky persuaded the Container Corporation of America to back him financially for the submitting of two paper geodesic domes to the Triennale contest. The domes, made of paperboard hexagons and an outer plastic skin, were assembled in the Sforza gardens in the city of Milan. And on the first night of the Triennale, when the lights were turned on inside one of the domes, the beauty of the geodesic pattern made visitors stop, mouths open in wonder.

Bucky's paperboard domes won the Grand Prize in Milan.

Now officials in both industry and government became aware of the power of the geodesic dome. Bucky received a letter from the Department of Commerce, asking if he could set up a dome for the United States Pavilion in the 1956 International Trade Fair to be held in the city of Kabul, Afghanistan. The dome he designed was one hundred feet across and thirty-five feet high. The speed with which illiterate native workers were able to erect it was stunning.

The Kabul Dome was the hit of the Fair. Not long after, similar domes began to appear at international fairs everywhere, from Poland to Japan. In different languages spoken all over the world, the word for *dome* began to be used more often. And usually spoken with the word for dome was the name Fuller.

At about the time that the Kabul Dome was being admired, an even greater success was in the making for Bucky. The famous industrialist Henry J. Kaiser, owner of one of the greatest aluminum companies in the country, decided that a hotel complex he owned in Honolulu, the *Hawaiian Village*, needed a concert auditorium. Hearing about the geodesic dome from one of his executives, Kaiser was impressed enough to ask Bucky for a license to manufacture a dome large enough to cover a 2,000 seat concert hall. In fact, Henry Kaiser became so excited about the possibilities of the geodesic dome that, with Bucky's permission, he tooled up an assembly line in his West Coast plant to manufacture aluminum domes.

Bucky designed a hundred-and-forty-five-foot-diameter dome for Kaiser and shipped the sections to Honolulu in February, 1957. Kaiser was most anxious to witness the erection of the dome. On the day that assembly was scheduled, he drove to the San Francisco airport and boarded a plane for Honolulu.

He was too late! To his great surprise, the first Kaiser dome was already raised and in place. That night, only twenty-two hours after unpacking, the Dome was filled with a capacity audience listening to a symphony concert!

After the news of the Hawaiian Dome spread through the building world, the Kaiser plant began to get calls for domes of all sizes. These became banks, theaters, and restaurants. One of their largest domes, about two hundred feet across, was sent to be the United States exhibit at the 1959 World's Fair in Moscow. It was the hit of the show. Nikita Khrushchev, then head of the Communist Party in the Soviet Union, made headlines with a famous blooper in which he mixed up Bucky's name. After expressing his delight over the Dome, Mr. Krushchev said to reporters, "I want Mr. J. Buckingham Fuller to come to the Soviet Union to teach our engineers!"

June 29, 1954, was the date that marked the real change in Bucky's career. On that day, the United States Patent Office issued Patent No. 2,682,235 in Bucky's name, putting him in control of the manufacturing of all geodesic structures in the country.

His days of struggle and failure were over. All obstacles to success were gone. Now he would be able to repay Anne for her long years of doing without and making the best of things. Now he could repay his family and his friends for their help and support in the past.

At last the world seemed to be aware of this sixty-year-old man, this impossible dreamer of things to come, this writer of incomprehensible words, this college drop-out —

This Buckminster Fuller had achieved instant genius!

10
Success at Sixty

THE SUDDEN recognition that came to Bucky as he approached his sixtieth birthday might have proved overwhelming for an ordinary man. Becoming wealthy almost overnight often makes it difficult for a man to keep his head.

But strangely enough, as the money rolled in faster and faster, it seemed to have less and less importance for Bucky. True, it was a relief to be able to settle all his old debts and to repay family and friends for help in the past. And it was nice to be able to say to Anne and Allegra, "Go into any store in the world and buy anything you want!" And he could see to it that the houses on Bear Island were fixed up and maintained regularly, so that the family could enjoy comfortable summers there.

But the most important thing now was that he could afford to travel anywhere in the world and talk to people about his ideas for providing man with all the benefits that could be derived from creative designing. In fact, he began to receive requests from universities, professional groups, and governments all over the world to come and speak and teach.

By 1959, more than a hundred companies had been licensed to manufacture geodesic domes. Some of these were "plydomes," made of bent pieces of plywood and used as playhouses in parks and playgrounds. Others were huge affairs, costing as much as two hundred thousand dollars each. The Union Tank Car Company built and installed such a dome, three hundred and eighty-four feet across, at Baton Rouge, Louisiana. This dome, which could accommodate an entire football field and stadium, was large enough for whole trainlengths of railroad cars that needed rebuilding. A similar dome was built at Woods River, Illinois. There was a geodesic dome over the Anheuser-Busch Park aviary in Tampa, Florida, and another over that dolphin playground, the Seaquarium, at Miami. In a Cape Cod restaurant, delicious seafood was served up under one of Bucky's domes. And in St. Louis, Missouri, a paradise of tropical foliage and flowers began to flourish in a temperature and humidity controlled atmosphere under a great aluminum and plastic dome called the *Climatron*. In addition to designing and consulting fees, Bucky's corporations received five per cent of the sales price of every dome made by a licensed manufacturer.

Airline stewardesses all over the world began to recognize the chunky man with the thick glasses who seemed to be going from one country to another throughout the year. No matter how long the flight, his temper was always even and his smile pleasant. He traveled several thousand miles in a jet as calmly as other men might drive down to the corner drugstore.

The message that Bucky brought to the universities he

visited and to the students whom he addressed was always about the part they would play in the future of man's existence on earth. He warned against overspecialization — that was the path to doom for mankind. Look at the different biological species that had disappeared from the face of the earth. Look at the human tribes that had become extinct. They had grown overspecialized, each in its own way — and could not adapt to sudden change.

This was precisely what Bucky's business was — being ready for change before it came. His name for this activity was *comprehensive anticipatory design science*. But politicians and industrialists had no interest in this kind of science. They cared little about the *ecology* of man, that is, about the balance between man and his natural surroundings. Look at the atmospheric pollution in the cities. Witness the wholesale destruction of forests and the indiscriminate use of insecticides. These were the results of specialization. Corporations were interested in specialization, because specialization provided them with a means of making money. Over and over, Bucky told his audiences:

"No scientist has ever been retained, or hired professionally, to consider the scientific design of the home of man, to consider objectively the ecological pattern of man, to design ways of employing the highest scientific potential towards helping man to be a success on earth, to implement total man to enjoy total earth. No scientist has ever been retained to do such a task. And we speak of our age as the *age of science!*"

It had taken the world almost thirty years to catch up

to Buckminster Fuller. Now, it seemed as though the world could not get its fill of him. He spoke at Capetown University in South Africa and at the Collegio degli Architecti (College of Architecture) in Milan, Italy. He visited England and Australia, Israel and Japan. Some of his domes were exhibited at the Metropolitan Museum and at the Museum of Modern Art in New York City. His honorary degrees, awarded at university and college graduations, began to pile up: Doctor of Design from North Carolina University, Doctor of Arts from the University of Michigan, Doctor of Science from Washington University. And all these for a man who had never completed his freshman year in college.

In 1959 he accepted an invitation from Southern Illinois University in Carbondale, Illinois, to become Research Professor of Design Science. His life's work had finally been recognized as a valid field of academic research.

He designed and built a beautiful blue and white geodesic dome house for himself and Anne. Allegra, already grown up and graduated from college, had married and lived in California. The University made few demands on Bucky's time; the president felt it was an honor just to have Bucky associated with them. He was able to adjust his life to a kind of steady pattern — two months or so in Carbondale, and the rest of the year traveling and working. He and Anne managed to be with Allegra at Christmas time; they usually saw the rest of the family during the summer. August became the "Bear Island month." There, with no telephone, Bucky could cut himself off from the world and relax completely.

The Carbondale house was always open to his many good friends. Whenever company came, he was still the gay Bucky of the old Greenwich Village days. He could always be prevailed upon to sing one or more of the funny parodies he wrote about domes and architects. To the tune of "Home on the Range," he would sing:

Let architects sing of aesthetics that bring
Rich clients in hordes to their knees;
Just give me a home in a great circle dome
Where the stresses and strains are at ease . . .

His energy amazed everyone who met him. A two-hour lecture, once begun, could easily go on for four or more hours. After-dinner conversation might finally end at three o'clock in the morning. This did not mean that he was simply a man who loved to hear the sound of his own voice. Bucky's marathon talking was really his way of thinking out loud. Once he began to speak, he never really knew when he would come up with some new idea during any lecture or conversation. It was difficult for older listeners without his superb stamina to keep up with him; young students seemed to be able to listen forever.

In 1960, the American Institute of Architects finally gave in. They conceded that R. Buckminster Fuller was worthy of recognition and made him an honorary life member. Of course, this was not the same as being a professional architect. In order to be able to submit legal contracts to dome licensees, Bucky had to take on a partner who was a registered architect. Only such a person could sign the contracts. He chose a brilliant young architect named Shoji Sadao and installed him in an office near the Massachusetts Institute of Technology in Cambridge.

Most older architects still found it difficult to accept Bucky. When asked, they would often reply that it was true Bucky was a man of genius, a great inventor, a fine engineer, "but he's not an architect, you know!"

On the other hand, Bucky was not afraid to tell young students of architecture what he thought was wrong with the profession. The architect, he pointed out, had sold himself down the river to the people who were making fortunes developing real estate. These operators hired architects, told them what kinds of houses to design, what materials were to be used, and where the materials would be purchased. The architect really designed nothing and originated nothing. He was just a slave to the real estate business.

What a young architect needed to know, Bucky said to his audience, was more than drawing, more than architecture. He had to go into airplane factories and learn about production engineering and tools and metal alloys. An architect without an understanding of the most advanced technology was a useless architect. For example, Bucky felt that chemistry was far more important to the architect than advanced mathematics; yet at most schools of architecture students often had little or no chemistry and three or four years of the calculus. But in chemistry was where you learned the rules by which nature structured materials, the materials that architects would be using in their work.

Architects, argued Bucky, had to become the opposite

of specialists. The specialist took things apart; the architect put things together. He was a *comprehensive* person. It was up to the architect to help keep the world from falling apart. But before he could do that, the teaching of architecture in the schools would have to change. Architecture would have to be taught as an important part of comprehensive anticipatory design science.

Bucky had a favorite way of describing the state of the civilized world. There were two major divisions of man's activity: *weaponry* and *livingry*. Major scientific advances had always been made in the name of weaponry. Thus, the armies of the world were equipped with costly electronic equipment for warning, destroying, and killing. But in the cities of the world, millions of people were still living in horrible slums. The peaceful arts that were concerned with improving man's shelter and well-being were low-priority arts, compared with the high priority of weaponry. So livingry was an underdeveloped area. Progress in livingry was made only in a kind of accidental way, as a by-product of the rapid technical advances made by weaponry. Perhaps this was one reason that engineers and scientists had lost communication with the people in literature and the fine arts.

"If you gain the lead in the world's design science," Bucky would tell his young audience, "and apply it to *livingry*, then there is hope. But you don't have much time. The weaponry industry is ready to invade the livingry field. If that happens, a dreadful fate awaits humanity. Man will become totally godless, and his life will be governed by decisions turned out by a computer. You the teachers, and you the students, are man's hope."

In 1963, when he was sixty-eight years old, Bucky received what many Americans considered a great recognition. His picture appeared on the cover of *Time* magazine.

Each year brought Bucky success piled on success. By 1966, more than five thousand domes had been installed in fifty countries. He now had acquired one hundred and forty-five patents, not only in America, but in fifty-five other countries. He had lectured and taught at two hundred universities and colleges in thirty countries.

His weekly program during the year was packed with detail. A typical section of the schedule looked something like this:

Wednesday, March 31:	Trip to India.
Sunday, April 11:	World Affairs Conference, Boulder, Colorado.
Thursday, April 22:	Keynote Speech for the World Congress of the International Center for the Typographic Arts, New York.
Wednesday, April 28:	Sail to England on the *Queen Mary*.
Monday, May 10:	Begin month as visiting professor at Bristol University, England.
Wednesday, June 23:	Address, Eighth Biennial World Congress, International Union of Architects, Paris, France.

Sunday, July 11:	Third Delos Symposium, Athens, Greece.
Saturday, July 17:	Return to New York and Carbondale.
August, all month:	Bear Island. No communication, except by mail.

Though Bucky's physical energy seemed endless, time did begin to take its toll. His hearing began to fail. But since he was Bucky Fuller, it did not fail in the ordinary way; that is, he did not just become more and more deaf. He simply began to hear some sounds less well than others. He tried hearing aids, but they only served to amplify all sound equally, and that was annoying. He found it most difficult to hear general conversation at a dinner party, where many people would be talking in different directions at once. All the sounds seemed to blend into a kind of ball of noise that made his head ache.

Eventually, he discovered an electronic device that helped. It was a large bullhorn that was a kind of directional antenna receiver and a loudspeaker combined. He could use it to make himself heard, or to catch specific sounds by pointing the horn in the proper direction. The bullhorn came in handy at conferences; before he got it, Bucky used to have to ask everyone to repeat what was being said. His eyes, of course, remained as bad as always. Because of them, he could never drive a car.

One of the interesting aspects of the geodesic dome was that as you made the dome larger and larger, the distances between vertices became smaller and smaller until the tetrahedral triangles virtually disappeared. You might say that in a dome of infinite size, the dome became virtually invisible.

This gave Bucky the idea of using a dome to cover an entire city. It was not a dream, but a possible actuality. He visualized a dome, two miles in diameter, covering part of the island of Manhattan in New York. A mile high, this dome would arch far above the Empire State Building. Bucky calculated the weight of this city covering at eighty thousand tons, to be assembled by helicopters in five-ton sections. The estimated cost was two hundred million dollars, not much money compared to what was being spent in the United States on weaponry.

Natural laws would provide a movement of air within the dome. The shell itself would be so strong that people could live *in* it, as well as under it. And since the network of such a large dome would be made of very small triangles, virtually a fine wire mesh, dwellers under the dome would see the sun in the day and the stars at night. What advantages would there be to living under the dome? No air pollution, no individual air-conditioners, no snow removal, no umbrellas, no colds.

Another of his plans was a home dome called "The Garden of Eden." This was a dome within a dome, with the inside dome covered by a transparent skin. Vines planted around the outside dome perimeter would climb up along the geodesic lines. A dweller in this house would see the sunlight streaming in through the green vine leaves. But the heat and bad weather would be kept out by the plastic skin. In fact, grooves could be made in the skin to capture the rain; this water could be diverted to water the vines, or even to fill a swimming pool.

The geodesic dome could give man the best chance to survive in his natural environment. But of course, Bucky saw that the major problem here was getting man to realize this. It was much easier to design a dome than to get men on earth to work together for their mutual happiness and prosperity.

One of the conferences Bucky was invited to attend was the Fourth Dartmouth Conference (so called, because the first was held at Dartmouth College) in the city of Leningrad in the Soviet Union. These conferences were actually a series of meetings between prominent American and Soviet citizens, and their purpose was to provide some kind of exchange of ideas and understandings between the two countries. Among those who attended were authors, scientists, businessmen, physicians, and other top men in different fields. They talked mostly about problems that were common to both countries, and how such problems could best be solved. The effect of belonging to two countries, each with a different system of government, showed up at once.

The Russians kept insisting that they had one advantage over the Americans in solving national problems. "We have a singleness of purpose in Russia. In America, everyone competes against everyone else; so the good effects cancel each other out." The Russian delegates really believed this, and the Americans found it difficult to prove that it was not so. The atmosphere of the meetings tended to grow cool and overpolite.

Bucky was given a whole afternoon in which to answer the Russian argument. As usual, he did not prepare a speech, but got up and began to think out loud on his feet. His first words shocked the Russians, for he said, "I don't know why I'm talking to you here, because you're all so ignorant!"

Then, before they could really feel insulted and walk out, he continued, "Many of you think of yourselves as scientists. But you go on a picnic with your families, and you see a lovely sunset, and you really *see* the sun setting! Now you have all had four hundred years to face up to the fact that the sun isn't setting at all — we learned that from Copernicus and Galileo — but that the sun is standing still, and the earth is rotating. I can make a model of the earth and paste a standing man on it, and in a few minutes I can convince any child that as the earth rotates, the man's shadow gets longer and longer, until the man is completely in the shadow. And that child will always think of what he sees in those terms.

"But you scientists still see the sun setting! What's worse, you talk about things being "down" or "up," when you really mean "in" or "out" in space. And you say that the wind is blowing from some direction — say, the northwest — when that isn't so at all. The real thing that's happening is that there is a low pressure area in the southeast, and the air is being sucked into that. So why don't you say that the wind is sucking southeast, which is the truth?"

By this time, the Russians had gotten the point, and they were shouting with laughter. Bucky had succeeded in breaking the ice. The rest of the meeting was carried on in an atmosphere of friendship. But he had not finished making his entire point.

"Young people are always asking me what it is like to be on a spaceship, and I always reply, 'You know what it feels like, you tell me!' Because we are living on a spaceship called the earth, a very small spaceship only eight thousand miles across. We've been living on it for a couple of million years. And the ecology of this spaceship is beautifully balanced, so that we can go on this way for a long, long time. The plants give up gases that are needed by mammals, and the mammals exhale gases that are needed by the plants.

"The bees are only interested in honey, and they go after it. And quite by accident they knock the pollen off with their little tails, and that fertilizes the flowers. Now, in the United States, we are all bees, and we are all really after our own honey, and quite by accident we knock off a lot of pollen, and so, quite by accident, we make a lot of contributions."

The Russians laughed again, and admitted that their argument about singleness of purpose might have been rather foolish. The solutions to man's important problems would come about quite independent of a single nation's politics.

Bucky went on to say what he really wanted to say to the Russians. Man had finally begun to know enough about his surroundings, his universe, so that he could actually begin to participate, instead of being an innocent victim of his own evolutionary changes. And this was no laughing matter.

"From now on, gentlemen," Bucky said, "man has to

be very responsible in all of his actions, or the show isn't going to work."

He was not only speaking to the Russians. He was speaking to the world.

11
Bucky Fuller, Poet and Prophet

In the year 1962, Harvard University recalled Buck-minster Fuller. But this time it was not as an under-graduate student.

He was asked to fill an honorary Chair and to become the Charles Eliot Norton Professor of Poetry. This pro-fessorship had been established to bring famous poets to the university for a two-month period during the school year, and the duty of each visiting professor was to give a series of lectures to students.

What did a world design scientist like Buckminster Fuller have to do with poetry? What did the geodesic dome have to do with rhymes and rhythm?

It had all begun many years before, when Bucky had been working for the Phelps Dodge Corporation. He had written a technical paper that was to be presented to the board of directors. One of the directors tried to read the paper. He sent it back to Bucky with a note saying that the paper just didn't make sense to him.

Bucky arranged to meet the man; patiently, he read the paper to him aloud, pausing every few moments to let the words sink in. "Why, that sounds just like poetry!"

cried the director. "Why don't you write it over again, just the way you read it to me?"

Bucky changed the lines of prose into lines of poetry, without changing any of the words, and resubmitted the paper to the board. Back it came with a message: the board of directors refused to read a poetical document.

Bucky protested that it wasn't really poetry at all, just his regular prose chopped up in order to make more sense. "Look," said the director, "I'm having a couple of poets up to the house for dinner tonight. I'll show them your paper and let them decide." The next day, he called Bucky. "No use, Fuller. They say it's poetry all right!" Back into prose form went the article.

From then on Bucky kept trying to put his thoughts into free verse. In 1940 he wrote a long poem, based on his feelings about how democracy should really work in the United States. This was the time when Hitler was threatening to overrun all of Europe. Bucky called the poem, "No More Secondhand God." Part of the poem read:

> *Many people believe Democracy obsolete.*
> *They are wrong.*
> *Obsolete is the one thing*
> *Democracy can never be,*
> *obstinate, obstreperous, observant, obscure, but —*
> *I will explain. That is, I will*
> *if it's Democracy you really wish to save,*
> *and not some trick you have been getting away with*
> *behind its kindly broad young back. . . .*

Even his complicated descriptions of what comprehensive anticipatory design science meant looked better and

sounded more understandable in poetic form. All you
had to do was compare the same passage written first as
prose and then as poetry:

> Thus, man is not the vegetable he eats, nor the
> water he drinks, nor the gases he breathes. Man is
> pure abstract integrity, made visible to other men
> by man-tuneable frequency relays of complexedly
> interlocking, but reciprocally accommodating, pat-
> terns representing every patterning principle of uni-
> verse cohering as the comprehensive integrity of pat-
> tern associabilities at mid-spectrum ranges, whose
> comprehensively and synergetically surprising re-
> sults are known to men as uniquely "individual"
> man.

Read aloud as lines of poetry, these same prose words
sounded beautiful and tended to have meaning, even if
you didn't understand all the words:

> *thus, man is not the vegetable he eats*
> *nor the water he drinks,*
> *nor the gases he breathes*
> *man is pure abstract pattern integrity*
> *made visible to other men*
> *by man-tuneable frequency relays*
> *of complexedly interlocking but*
> *reciprocally accommodating patterns —*
> *representing every patterning principle of universe*
> *cohering as the comprehensive integrity of*
> *pattern associabilities at mid-spectrum ranges*
> *whose comprehensively and synergetically*

surprising results
are known to men
as uniquely "individual" man . . .

No More Secondhand God was published as a book (along with other poems and some essays) by the Southern Illinois University Press. In 1962, another of Bucky's poems, this time a very long one, was also published in book form. Its title was *Untitled Epic Poem on the History of Industrialization.*

At Harvard University, during the months of February and March, Bucky delivered three lectures. Poet, inventor, architect — it made no difference to the students; Bucky was a tremendous success. In his own words, the Harvard concept of the word *poet* had little to do with a man who wrote poetry; by *poet* they really meant "man who puts things together." In that sense, Fuller the Comprehensive Man was qualified for the Norton Professorship of Poetry.

Bucky's activities and interests were so widespread during the early years of the 1960's, that he always seemed to be in ten places at once. One of the places was East St. Louis in Illinois, where Southern Illinois University was planning to establish a new city branch campus. Bucky was asked to speak to the planning committee, which was made up of college presidents, a city planner, a sociologist, a psychiatrist, and a landscape architect, each a famous person in his own field. Of course, R. Buckminster Fuller was himself a member of the committee.

In this talk (which was later published as a book called

Education Automation), Bucky presented his own ideas about what a university should be and what it should accomplish in the way of educating young people. He suggested that the United States would have to change its point of view about the education of its children. American education had declined from its early, ideal state to where it was now mainly being used by politicians as a means of achieving power. Meanwhile, the really pressing problems at hand were completely ignored. Bucky said:

"There is also a general baby-sitting function which is called school. While the children are being 'baby sat,' they might as well be given something to read. We find that they get along pretty well with the game of 'reading'; so we give them more to read, and we add writing and arithmetic. Very seriously, much of what goes on in our schools is strictly related to social experiences, and that is fine — that's good for the kids. But I would say that we are going to add much more in the near future by taking advantage of the children's ability to show us what they need."

He then pointed out how television could be used to bring education right into the home, and how computers were going to be used to fortify the learning process. What could the universities do? Their job would be to take education out of the hands of the politicians and to find solutions to the problems of educating our children through the use of total world planning. The sad fact was that the total resources of the earth were now being used to serve only forty-three per cent of humanity. Through the use of comprehensive anticipatory design science, all the resources of the world could be made to serve all humanity.

Changes in human society had to be *anticipated* and not dealt with as they happened. For example, it was inevitable that soon man would no longer have to use his muscles in order to make a living. Automation — the automatic control of all production machinery by computers — would take care of that. When that happened, what would have to be done? One important result would be that society would have to educate each and every one of its members. All people everywhere would have to be made literate by being sent to schools. Bucky was certain that education was going to become the major industry of the world.

In an effort to demonstrate his seriousness and his concern for the future, Bucky financed a research program at Southern Illinois to investigate how the world's natural resources were being used. He called his program a ten-year design (1965–1975) for "re-tooling" the world. This study would show specifically how all the chemical and energy resources of the world could be "rendered adequate to the service of one hundred per cent of humanity at higher standards of living and total enjoyment than any man has yet experienced."

Bucky asked John McHale, a visiting artist and designer from England, to be the executive director of the project. The research team was composed of two physicists, three design specialists, and an architect.

In 1963, the first report of *World Science Decade, 1965–1975*, was published. It included rafts of data about the distribution of world resources and world energy, all compiled and processed by computers. One table listed the world production of major minerals and metals, country by country. A group of maps showed the distribution of items like iron ore, coal, and waterpower over the surface of the earth. One of the most striking reports showed how at least half the world's people were really cut off from communication with the rest of the world; in these areas there were fewer than ten daily newspapers, five radio receivers, and two movie-theater seats for every hundred persons. Such cut-off places existed mainly on the continents of Asia, Africa, and South America — the less industrialized parts of the world.

Bucky's research team also noted that the solution for this problem of noncommunication could well be provided by mass world education. Television, moving pictures, and computerized teaching, all linked together with the new understandings psychologists had achieved about people and learning, were now available to make the job easier. The report noted further: "It is well to remember that the comprehensive world economics are going to force vast economic reforms of industries and nations which incidentally will require utter modernization of the educational processes in order to survive . . . As we effectively disemploy man as a mechanical worker and pay him to return to his studies this will bring about profound changes in our concept of education itself. Education 'to earn a living' will become an anachronism . . ."

Also included in the report was a grand lecture entitled, "World Design Initiative," given by Bucky to a large audience of professional architects and architecture students at the International Symposium on Architecture held in Mexico. In this talk (in true Fuller style, the printed manuscript ran about a hundred pages), Bucky presented the development of his natural synergetic geometry and told how the geodesic dome had been born. He urged all the visiting architects and the students who were listening to devote their lives to furthering the cause of "livingry," even if that meant departing from accepted patterns of professional behavior.

"I am convinced," said Bucky, "that it is only man's inertial ignorance and its superstition-conditioned reflexes that bind him, unrealistically, within the nonsensical illusion of conformity." By that, he meant that men tended to lose their fears of change and the unknown very slowly. Rather than meet the challenge of change head-on with the new power that science and technology now afforded, older generations hesitated to break with the traditions of the past that held them captive.

Such messages of hope and change became part and parcel of Bucky's world career. As always, these messages were addressed to university students everywhere.

In June 1965, the year of his seventieth birthday, Bucky sat in his rooms in Bristol, England, where he was a visiting professor at the University of Bristol, and wrote a short essay called, "Utopia or Oblivion."

In it, he pointed out that man now had for the first time the actual possibility of achieving utopia — or the perfect world — in his grasp. On the other hand, the chance that he would destroy himself and the whole world was equally possible. Which was it to be? How was the choice to be made?

The large percentage of human beings on earth, he wrote, have failed to see and understand the full significance of the new technological revolution. Only one per cent of the world's population were scientists, and the other ninety-nine per cent were hopelessly out of communication with them.

Also, history showed plainly that control, first of the seas and then of the land, was accomplished by one per cent of the total population, while the rest of humanity seemed to be unaware of what was happening. The powerful "masters" of society could and did hire inventors, scientists, and engineers to perfect the technology that was used to hold power. Much of what went on could be hidden from the public in the name of national defense secrecy. In the name of that same "defense," the "masters" could use most of the new science and technology to create and stockpile the final tools of man's own destruction — weaponry.

But those students who had begun to study and to understand the whole point of world design science were also beginning to see that there was a critical need to change this pattern of world control.

Bucky Fuller knew students. Better yet, he could see the world through the eyes of young students. Even though he was now seventy, he was still a member of every student generation. He wrote:

"The student knows that man can do anything he wants. Yet they see world officialdom investing the world's highest capabilities only in race suicide springboards!"

Students all over the world were becoming restless.

They were becoming dissatisfied with the inadequacies of past ways of coping with the pressing problems of mankind. They were becoming aware that many people on earth were still starving, while billions of dollars and millions of man-hours of work were being wasted on weapons and war.

And those students who were in college during the early 1960's were a special group. Many of the graduate students had been born while their fathers were away at war. The undergraduates had cut their eyeteeth on television which had put them directly in touch with the entire world. They knew the world as one in which science and technology had made possible inventions to surmount all the barriers of nature. Their birthmark was the atom bomb. So their dissatisfactiion with the way the world was being controlled was logical and genuine. They knew that to change this way was their destiny.

If the students could persuade the adult world that such a change was necessary, the world might yet be saved. Bucky wrote these words with all the hope an optimist could muster. If the students could manage to win such support from adult wage earners within the next ten years, he wrote, man might yet continue on earth. Because of the students' intuition and youth, the chances were good.

Unfortunately the people in charge of affairs in the various countries — the bankers, businessmen, and politicians — had not understood the message of world design science. They seemed to want to keep the world as disunited as possible. To Bucky, these men in the different countries of the world, democracy or dictatorship, seemed to be carrying on a kind of game-playing. Each country boasted of its own inventiveness, of its own national wealth, or its own national industrialization.

This kind of political ballyhoo was nonsense to Bucky. He did not have faith in *national* man. He could only see an *international* man, a character he called *continuous man*. It was continuous man, American and Russian, Swede and Brazilian, who could really run things while the politicians, both capitalist and communist, played out their little national games. It was the job of continuous man to make the world work. He was the one to make all of humanity consumers of the marvels that science and technology would produce.

And Bucky Fuller had dedicated himself to keeping continuous man alive forever.

12
Living Space for *World Man*

In 1927 two scientists working in the Bell Telephone Research Laboratories had found that electrons behaved like light waves. This was a most interesting kind of contrary behavior, for up until that time, electrons seemed to be particles (you could picture them, perhaps, like little electrified marbles), and there was no reason for them to behave like waves. But the two experimenters, Davisson and Germer, had evidence that could not be denied.

About ten years later, their discovery became the basis for an invention called the electron microscope. This instrument used magnets to focus beams of electrons, just as glass lenses focused light rays in optical microscopes. The magnifying power was tremendous; the electron microscope made it possible to see things that had never been seen before. By the end of the 1950's, electron microscopy had improved to the point where scientists were taking highly magnified photographs of viruses, the tiniest forms of life known to exist.

What did the electron microscope have to do with Buckminster Fuller?

Simply this: the biophysicists and molecular biologists, using their electron microscopes, found that all viruses were essentially built like geodesic domes!

Every known virus has a kind of outside shell made of protein molecules. Bucky's geodesic dome formulas predicted exactly the geometric structure of every known virus. Pieces of animal tissue, magnified more than fifty thousand times, showed their cell structures to be constructed of tetrahedral patterns. The cornea of the human eye looked just like a geodesic tensegrity structure. An electron microscope photo of a diatom, one of those tiny sea plants, looked exactly like the top of the Union Tank Car Company Dome!

Nuclear physicists, probing deeply into the structure of the atomic nucleus, began to come up with evidence that Bucky's natural geometry seemed to apply to that most fundamental of all structures. Using tetrahedrons, Bucky could give a reasonable explanation for the action of DNA, the molecular structure that seemed to be responsible for passing on biological characteristics through the genes.

One result of such new findings was that academic specialists began to listen to Bucky with a new respect. Slowly, he began to be drawn into the scientific establishment that had excluded him for so many years. One token of "belonging" was his appointment as Distinguished Scientist at the United States Institute of Behavioral Research. Another was his being engaged as special consultant to NASA, the government agency responsible for all space flights.

In 1964, the State of New York commissioned Bucky

to fashion a colorful dome for their State Pavilion at the World's Fair that was to be held later that year on the site of the famous 1939 World's Fair in Flushing. And two years later he received an order that was to result in one of the most magnificent domes ever designed.

The United States government asked him to design a dome that would be the American Pavilion at the Canadian World's Fair in 1967. This Fair was to be held in Montreal, to celebrate the one hundredth anniversary of Canada's becoming a dominion. At the same time, the city of Montreal would be celebrating its 325th birthday. For this great Fair, named "Expo 67," an entirely new, artificial island was created in the St. Lawrence River to hold the pavilions and exhibits of seventy nations.

Bucky took the problem of designing the dome to his group of young architects and designers from Harvard University and the Massachusetts Institute of Technology known as the "Cambridge Seven." They came up with a brilliant design. The dome would be a huge plastic bubble, two hundred and fifty feet across. It would dramatize the exhibits inside, a panorama called *Creative America*. Bucky rolled up his sleeves and joined them in the planning of the dome.

From the complicated blueprints there first emerged a large scale model. It was a kind of "three-quarters" bubble, whose light steel framework was made of hexagons. Instead of a whole plastic skin, Bucky's team designed a covering made of thousands of separate, plastic hexagons. These were arranged on pivots, so that they could turn individually. A network of motors, over two hundred and fifty of them, was set up to open and close the plastic hexagons. This motor network, in turn, was regulated by a computer that was programmed to trigger the motor in response to outside weather conditions. Thus, some of the hexagons might close to keep the sun out, while others might open to let it in. Some of the hexagons had light sensors, and these sensors opened or closed shades, depending upon the amount of light that hit them. Other hexagons had intake and exhaust valves to regulate the amount of fresh air inside the dome.

The result was an American Pavilion unlike any ever constructed before. Bucky's dome appeared to the visitors of Expo 67 as a kind of living creature. Different parts of the skin of the dome kept changing colors during the day, sometimes silver, sometimes transparent, sometimes like a rainbow. From inside the dome, people could see the clouds in the sky. But the light that came into the dome was soft, shaded light.

Inside the dome, which was two hundred feet high, there was a series of platforms, staggered at different heights and linked by escalators. Visitors rode up and down from platform to platform viewing the exhibits inside and marveling at the dome structure. Everyone who went through the dome agreed that the dome itself was far more exciting an adventure than the exhibits inside. At night, interior lighting turned the dome into a beautiful, glowing sphere, a modern Taj Mahal that was the most magnificent spot in the entire fairgrounds.

When Expo 67 closed its gates, the city of Montreal purchased the American Pavilion, which became a permanent fixture of a complex display called "Man and the World." Bucky's dome is now an aviary filled with beautiful birds.

You would think that a man at the age of seventy-two

would have had enough of striving and failure. You would think that a man who had finally achieved an annual income of several hundred thousand dollars and international fame would want to stop working. You would think that such a man would be glad to quit, to rest, to place the baton in younger hands and leave the race.

Not Buckminster Fuller.

There was still too much to be done. There was the work of the international teams who were cooperating in the World Design Inventory. There were the students to be taught at Southern Illinois University. There were the hours to be spent in jet planes flying from lecture to lecture, from visiting professorship to visiting professorship. And above all, there was the need to keep the cause of livingry going.

Most of all, Bucky worried about the problems of city life in America. American cities had ceased to develop progressively. During the early years of the 1960's, it had become apparent to all who lived in or visited them that most large American cities were in terrible shape.

Attempts to eliminate city slums had failed. Even though new housing projects had been erected for slum dwellers, these people remained poor. The housing projects simply became new slums. Crime in the cities increased. In most large cities it was unsafe to walk the streets at night. City parks that had once teemed with people on hot nights had become deserted, empty areas that were only shadowy invitations to violence and robbery.

Those city dwellers who could afford to move did so. They fled to the suburbs in droves. The inner parts of the cities became a combination of slums and business sections. The latter were usually canyons of massive stone and glass office buildings. City streets, never planned for automobiles, were choked with traffic day and night.

Bucky saw this lack of city planning as the fault of the political and industrial "masters" and the architects. Any new buildings built in cities like New York or Chicago were planned only on the basis of how much money each would earn for its owner. In an article written for the *Saturday Review,* Bucky pointed out that the first question house-builders asked was: how many people will live in this building, and how much will the rent total?

Next, the necessary number of elevator shafts to accommodate the maximum number of dwellers were planned. These shafts became the major space around which the building was raised. Engineers were hired to design the steel skeleton and all the power systems. Interior and exterior decorators made decisions about windows, lighting fixtures, paint colors, and so on. What did the architect do?

Actually, wrote Bucky, very little. He acted as a kind of purchasing agent for the building owners. He "sort-of organized" the building space. The most important functions were really carried out by the engineers. The architect had lost his most important job — being a planner. Now, he was only a salesman for his firm.

This failure to use the architect as a designer and planner was part and parcel of Bucky's complaint that the resources of the world were being used for the benefit of less than fifty per cent of humanity. The existence of national barriers plus the fears aroused by nationalism was preventing the use of all man's capabilities for the good of all men. Perhaps the coming of the computer might afford a solution. Perhaps the politicians and the "masters," who would not listen to the design scientists — or to one another, for that matter — would listen to the computer. Because the computer, after digesting all the facts that were fed into it, would only tell them the truth. And the truth was that man had to stop competing with machines. Man had to begin using the machines *to do more with less.*

One of the most interesting persons Bucky had met during his travels was a wealthy Japanese businessman named Masutaro Shoriki. His wealth had come originally from the rapid expansion of a newspaper he had purchased when it had a small circulation. Mr. Shoriki apparently had a feeling for what kind of news the public enjoyed. Also, he was aware that modern technology had come to stay. He purchased one of the largest offset presses in the world, so that he could run off large numbers of newspapers very quickly. It did not take Mr. Shoriki very long to become an important man in Japanese social life and politics.

After World War II, Mr. Shoriki helped the new Japanese government get back on its feet. He used many clever ideas to help restore the economy that had been ruined by warfare and defeat. One thing he did was to help the government reopen a large racetrack that began to show a profit at once. Mr. Shoriki helped bring both television and baseball to Japan.

But as the Japanese millionaire grew older, he felt that he should try to accomplish something more meaningful than his past local successes. He wanted to help Japan make an important contribution to the world. And what interested Masutaro Shoriki most was the unsolved problem of housing the people of the world. How could every person on earth be housed adequately? How could every person on earth enjoy a high and meaningful standard of living?

In order to accomplish this task, Mr. Shoriki commissioned Bucky Fuller to design and develop a city for a million people.

How do you go about planning such a city? What are the first questions to be asked? What do you have to know? What are the dangers to be avoided?

Bucky handed the problem over to the architects and scientists who had designed the Expo 67 dome. After mulling things over for a while, they decided that all the available information about cities and city life ought to be put into statistical form and analyzed by computer. This was begun. It was a formidable task, taking weeks and months of hard work and much of Mr. Shoriki's money; but eventually it was finished.

After comparing the various kinds of data, the computer printed out a series of mathematical results that could be interpreted as composing a "converging complex." What did that mean? Simply, it was what had to be put together to make an entire city.

The next part of the operation was more difficult.

Where was the best location for such a complex — land, sea, or air? How large ought the complex to be for the most efficient operation? What kind of social planning and economic structure should this operation have? These questions and many more had to be answered before the actual designing began.

It was going to take a long time to complete this part. But Bucky had already begun to think ahead about the design he favored. What was that design?

Naturally, a tetrahedron.

Bucky thought that a floating city, like a great, anchored iceberg, would be best. He visualized a great pyramid, a tetrahedron, floating in the waters of Tokyo Bay. It could all work very efficiently. The power for the city would come from atomic engines. City wastes could be used as fuel to generate energy for a desalinization plant designed to remove the salt and impurities from bay water and to feed a continuous supply of fresh water into the city. A side product of that plant would be enough energy to furnish cheap electric power.

One of the wonderful effects of using a tetrahedral shape was that the city could actually imitate nature. Crystals in nature grow larger by adding on little tetrahedral cells. In this way, the crystals acquired the largest possible surface for the smallest possible volume. And so, a tetrahedral city could begin with any size, and, like a crystal, add on little tetrahedrons to increase the overall size of the original tetrahedron. The only limit was convenience.

Imagine a huge floating pyramid made of great shelves. House units, or apartments, could be mass-produced and placed on these shelves. The whole pyramid could be easily assembled, or disassembled, in parts, like a child's toy. For example, if one household wanted to leave Tokyo Bay for a few weeks of vacation, their dwelling could be lifted out, placed on the water and hitched to a motorboat.

There were so many possibilities in this kind of design. A tetrahedral city might begin small, about ten or fifteen stories high, housing only a hundred thousand people. But the city could easily grow, tetrahedron by tetrahedron, until it reached a mile or more in height and could house a million people.

It was Bucky's feeling that Japan was an ideal place to carry out this anticipatory design of a city of the future. The United States had not yet seemed to see the handwriting on the wall that said its cities, in their present states, were doomed. Americans talked about the problems of the cities; but the attacks on these problems up until now had been small and futile. It was like fighting cancer with aspirin and Band-aids. Perhaps Japan would show the United States the way by supporting this great effort to anticipate the future. Mr. Shoriki's dream of bringing humanity together in a vast effort to improve the life of every person on earth might yet come true.

Bucky Fuller was looking ahead to the time when this would happen, when no man on earth would look upon any other man as his mortal enemy. He was anticipating the coming of a man who would be at home anywhere on earth — a *world man*.

Wichita house, or Dymaxion dwelling machine

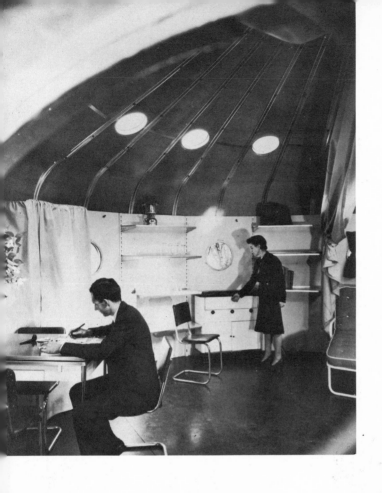

Above, kitchen of the Dymaxion dwelling. Left, the bathroom, top half removed

Launching the first Dymaxion Car

The Ford Rotunda Dome

The first airlift of a shelter

Dome of the U.S. Pavilion at the Kabul, Afghanistan, Trade Fair

Buckminster Fuller before the Kaiser
Dome, Solkoniki Park, Moscow, U.S.S.R.

Dome on top of Mount Washington

Left, inside Shaw Garden's Climatron, St. Louis. Below, minirail train coming out of U.S. Pavilion bubble at Expo '67, Montreal

Right, child climbing
Playdome. Below, vaca-
tion house

Left, Triennale Dome, Italy. Below, Union Tank Car shop, Baton Rouge, Louisiana

Tetrahedronal city model, Triton City

Buckminster Fuller, at home with models

The End—but Not the End

THROUGH the windows of The Big House the soft ocean wind swam, bringing smells of salt and sea things. Mixed in was the balsam smell of the pine trees. The same wind lifted the drooping American flag and stretched it proudly away from the top of the flagpole. On the other side of the island, the wind blew through the bare bones of the large model of a tensegrity dome.

In the living room with the great stone fireplace, the children of Bear Island were gathered. Some were Bucky's great-nephews and nieces; others were the children of Captain Hardie, the Island caretaker; a few were the children of the guests of the moment. It was early afternoon; the adults were still taking their after-dinner siestas. Only the children were there — the children and Uncle Bucky.

The seventy-year-old face turned to the faces that had not yet seen ten years pass. Behind the thick glasses, his eyes, turned owlish by the lenses, gleamed.

He knew that the world of men was at that moment in a sorry state. He had seen his country pass through two world-devastating wars. And those had not served to bar war from the earth. There had been a serious conflict in the country of Korea. At that very moment, a new death struggle was going on in the jungles of Vietnam. The United Nations Organization had not united the peoples of the earth.

He knew that because there had been no advance planning the cities of his country were in a state of decay. He knew that the poor of the slums and the poor of the fields were beginning to strike out openly for the right, not just to survive, but to enjoy the best that life had to offer.

And he knew that he had opened the way for that right to come true for everyone in the world.

"Children," he said. "Children, let's begin."

The chattering stopped; they all knew the signal. Learning with Uncle Bucky was almost as good as play. It was fun.

"This afternoon, we'll have a lesson about boxes. Now look at these soft, red plastic straws I have here. They fit into the holes in these flexible rubber connectors. First, let's make a house like the ones we see everywhere. It's a square box that we call a cube. What happens when I put the cube on the floor?"

Everyone saw at once. "It falls down, Uncle Bucky!"

"Yes, you all saw — a cube made of flexible parts cannot stand by itself! But now, I'll reshape that box into a triangle shape called a tetrahedron. Let's say that word together: tet-ra-hed-ron!"

They called it out together, the littlest ones stumbling over the syllables as best they could.

"Now, I am going to place the tetrahedron on the floor. Does it behave like the cube? What's the difference?"

He watched the young faces light up with delight. They knew what the difference would be. He could teach them to see and understand what too many people in the world could not.

Bucky Fuller smiled and nodded his head.

He was talking to the future.

Bibliography

THE AUTHOR is indebted to the following works for information about R. Buckminster Fuller:

Jacobs, David, "An Expo Named Buckminster Fuller." *New York Times Magazine*, April 23, 1967.

Marks, Robert W., *The Dymaxion World of Buckminster Fuller*. Reinhold, 1960.

McHale, John, *R. Buckminster Fuller*. Braziller, 1962.

Tomkins, Calvin, "In the Outlaw Area." *The New Yorker*, January 8, 1966.

The following books are by R. Buckminster Fuller:

Education Automation: Freeing the Scholar to Return to His Studies. Southern Illinois University Press, Carbondale, Illinois, 1963.

Ideas and Integrities. Prentice-Hall, New York, 1963.

Nine Chains to the Moon. Southern Illinois University Press, Carbondale, Illinois, 1963.

No More Secondhand God and Other Writings. Southern

Illinois University Press, Carbondale, Illinois, 1963.

Operating Manual for Spaceship Earth. Southern Illinois University Press, Carbondale, Illinois, 1969.

Untitled Epic Poem on the History of Civilization. Jonathan Williams, Charlotte, North Carolina, 1962.